FOUNDATIONS OF MODERN BIOLOGY SERIES

Animal

Diversity

EARL D. HANSON

Wesleyan University

Prentice-Hall, Inc.

ENGLEWOOD CLIFFS, NEW JERSEY

1961

Animal Diversity

Earl D. Hanson

PRENTICE-HALL FOUNDATIONS OF MODERN BIOLOGY SERIES

William D. McElroy and Carl P. Swanson, *Editors*

Design by Walter Behnke

Drawings by Felix Cooper

C

Foundations of Modern Biology Series

The science of biology today is *not* the same science of fifty, twenty-five, or even ten years ago. Today's accelerated pace of research, aided by new instruments, techniques, and points of view, imparts to biology a rapidly changing character as discoveries pile one on top of the other. All of us are aware, however, that each new and important discovery is not just a mere addition to our knowledge; it also throws our established beliefs into question, and forces us constantly to reappraise and often to reshape the foundations upon which biology rests. An adequate presentation of the dynamic state of modern biology is, therefore, a formidable task and a challenge worthy of our best teachers.

The authors of this series believe that a new approach to the organization of the subject matter of biology is urgently needed to meet this challenge, an approach that introduces the student to biology as a growing, active science, and that also *permits each teacher of biology to determine the level and the structure of his own course.* A single textbook cannot provide such flexibility, and it is the authors' strong conviction that these student needs and teacher prerogatives can best be met by a series of short, inexpensive, well-written, and well-illustrated books so planned as to encompass those areas of study central to an understanding of the content, state, and direction of modern biology. The FOUNDATIONS OF MODERN BIOLOGY SERIES represents the translation of these ideas into print, with each volume being complete in itself yet at the same time serving as an integral part of the series as a whole.

v

Preface

This book is written on the assumption that for a reader to comprehend a topic, he must be presented not only with factual material but with that material organized into systematic form. In presenting the subject of this book —animal diversity—therefore, I have attempted to sift and arrange the facts into a meaningful system.

Thus this book is *not* an introductory survey of classificatory zoology; it is *not* intended as a brief, descriptive compendium of animal morphology. It does deal with these subjects, but the aim is to go beyond the descriptive level to the analytical and explanatory stage—to see how a biologist might try to explain animal diversity and not just describe it. To attempt this, within such a small volume, is perhaps foolhardy. But the author is convinced that the study of science at the introductory adult level— where this book is directed—must basically pursue the conscious goal of exploring the nature of human understanding. Hence this book approaches animal diversity in such a context and strives to so organize facts as to give the reader a broad perspective of our present knowledge of animal diversity.

Earl D. Hanson

Contents

7

8

1

Understanding Animal Diversity

The need to understand is inherent in man. Human nature requires that we continually try to order our experience so as to comprehend it. This is true both of our experience of the external world around us and of the inner world of self. In this short book, we shall try to organize our experience of that part of the external world composed of animals and thus attempt to gain some understanding of it. Before turning to the study of animals, however, let us consider what is meant by understanding. An experience may be said to be understood when it can be explained, that is, when an explanatory statement regarding it has been made, tested, and found acceptable. But what do we mean by the terms, "explanatory statement," "tested," and "acceptable"? Their definitions are best revealed by a discussion of scientific methodology.

The scientific method refers simply to what humans do in trying to understand scientific problems. It is a complex process, and its procedures are not rigidly set, despite attempts to make it into a formula. A scientist must, however, do three things, whatever they may be called, if he is systematically to search for solutions. First, he must *formulate the problem*. To do this, of course, he must begin with an awareness of the problem, simply be curious about a gap in our scientific knowledge. Why some minds sense a problem and others do not remains a mystery. A sensitive curiosity, in

1

any case, is a prerequisite for scientific work. The scientist's puzzlement should next lead him to describe the problem with meticulous care and, if possible, in quantitative terms. Precision is crucial, not only for its own sake, but because the more precise the question, the more likely is the chance that a valid answer will be forthcoming.

The second essential part of all scientific activity consists of *proposing an hypothesis*. An hypothesis is a provisional explanatory statement expressing a possible relationship of the unsolved problem to other, already tested and accepted, statements. It is an attempt to solve a problem by logically relating it to previously established knowledge. (This is what was meant above by the phrase, "order our experience"; thus hypotheses play a key role in that process.) An hypothesis should suggest results that will follow if the hypothesis is correct. These expected results are called predictions; without predictions an hypothesis cannot be tested and is therefore of little use.

The third part of scientific activity is *testing the hypothesis*. Observations are made to determine whether or not the predictions are fulfilled. Experiments are often set up to check new data or a re-examination is undertaken of old information. Note that we are here testing the consequences of the hypothesis, not the hypothesis itself, as is often supposed. After completing his tests, the scientist must conclude whether to accept the hypothesis, if the predictions are realized, or reject it, if the predictions are not realized, and then decide what the next step should be.

These three phases of scientific activity may be illustrated by a simple example. Needing a flashlight, we grab one and flick the switch, but *no* light is produced. After pondering this a moment, we form the explanation or hypothesis, on the basis of previous experience, that the bulb is the most likely source of trouble. We unscrew the bulb, drop it in the wastebasket, and screw in a fresh one. But the light still does not work, despite our thumpings and mutterings. We try the new bulb in a second flashlight, and it works. Digging the original bulb out of the wastebasket, we find that it, too, works in the second flashlight. We reject our first hypothesis and form a new one: the batteries are worn out. After inserting fresh batteries into the first flashlight, we flick the switch and it works.

How does this example illustrate the scientific method as we have described it? Our awareness of the problem arose with the initial failure of the flashlight, which, in fact, probably generated more irritation than it did curiosity. Instead of asking helplessly, "Now what's wrong?", we quickly reviewed how a flashlight works and arrived at the first hypothesis: the bulb was burned out. We tested this hypothesis by replacing the bulb. A second bulb didn't work, so we discarded the hypothesis, postulated a new one, tested it by replacing the batteries, and found it was correct. In this everyday example, some of the steps may be taken unconsciously.

Our experience with the flashlight points up two things. First, one can apply the scientific method without being a specialist who peers through a microscope or a telescope; the scientific method depends on the ability to receive sensory data and to think logically, capacities that are common to all normal people. Much of our daily activity, therefore, falls into a pattern that could be called scientific. The second conclusion is that it is not what we work with that makes us scientists—anyone can look at stars, mix different solutions, or preserve rare animals—it is *how* we do it that counts. If we use the scientific method, consciously or unconsciously, to analyze some aspect of nature, then we are scientists. How good a scientist depends on motivation, training, and experience. The prepared mind discovers the most promising problems; the trained intelligence constructs the most fruitful hypotheses; and the skilled researcher is the most successful and ingenious experimenter.

This book will employ the scientific method to increase our understanding of animals and the reason for their diversity. Part Two formulates the problem of animal diversity. Part Three presents an explanatory hypothesis for this diversity and outlines certain predictions stemming from that hypothesis. In the three chapters of Part Four, which contain the bulk of the book's factual information, the predictions are tested. Finally, the concluding chapter evaluates our success in explaining the problem of animal diversity.

By applying this approach, we hope to do more than just describe animal diversity; we hope also to explain it, at least in part. As we shall see, however, many questions remain unanswered. But perhaps we shall be able to discern, even if dimly, the extent of our knowledge about animal diversity. How much do we really know about it? How much can we expect to know on the basis of our present information? What are the new questions we should be asking ourselves? Our intent, then, is to clarify the achievement and limitations manifested by scientific activity in the study of that part of our world composed of animal forms.

2

**The
Diversity
of
Animals**

The purpose of this chapter is to present a brief sample of the variety of animal forms, so that we can get an idea of the extent of this variety and of the terms used to describe it.

There is a ten-millionfold difference in size between the smallest living organism commonly considered to be an animal and the largest one. The largest known animals are the whales, and among these the blue whale is the biggest, reaching a maximum length of around 100 feet. The smallest living animals are probably the spores, or so-called resting stages, of certain tiny parasites, the Microsporida, which are 3 to 6 microns in their largest diameter. Since one micron equals about 1/25,000 of an inch, and since a 100-foot blue whale is 1,200 inches long, we readily see that a big blue whale is 10,000,000 or 10^7 times longer than the smallest microsporidian spore.

Figure 1 gives specific data on different kinds of animals: their actual size, and their size relative to a 100-foot blue whale and to a microsporidian 3 microns in diameter. The smallest viruses, which are the smallest living things known (for example, the foot-and-mouth disease virus), are 1/300 the size of the microsporidian spore, and the largest living things we know, the redwood trees of California, stand at a height from the ground that is roughly three times the length of the blue whale (and their weight is correspondingly heavier).

4

Figure 1

Relative sizes of selected animals.

	Average size	Relative to blue whale	Relative to microsporidian
Blue whale	100 feet	1	10,000,000
African elephant	11 feet °	0.11	1,100,000
Man	5 feet 8 inches	0.056	567,000
Gorilla	5 feet 5 inches	0.055	542,000
Dog (cocker spaniel)	2 feet	0.02	200,000
Pigeon	15 inches	0.013	125,000
Lobster	12 inches	0.01	100,000
Jellyfish	8 inches	0.0067	67,000
Starfish	7 inches	0.0058	58,000
Earthworm	6 inches	0.005	50,000
Grasshopper	1½ inches	0.0013	13,000
Amoeba	500 microns	0.000017	167
Microsporidian spore	3 microns	0.00000001	1

°Shoulder height.

A cautious guess would be that around 1,200,000 different kinds or species of animals have been described by man. This means that man can recognize well over a million unique forms. But it should be realized that many species show more than one distinct form (Fig. 2). There may be differences between males and females of a single species. There are differences in form between the young and adults, as exemplified by a caterpillar and its adult form, the butterfly. There are different stages of life cycles, especially in parasitic forms, of which we shall see examples later. And then there are differences between individuals of any given species, not only in form but also in coloration. If we disregard this last category of differences, we should multiply the known number of species by at least a factor of two and probably by a factor several times that to achieve a rough quantitative approximation of the varieties of animal form. In other words, there are probably several million distinct animal forms.

What are some of the ways in which this variety of form is expressed? Let us deal first just with external form, and begin with the concept of symmetry. By symmetry in animals we mean the arbitrary division of animals into essentially mirror halves on opposite sides of an imaginary dividing plane (Fig. 3). Certain animals show no symmetry; the amoeba (Fig. 3a), is asymmetrical, for its opposite sides do not match. Most animals show *bilateral symmetry,* that is, their bodies can be divided by one and only one imaginary plane into right and left halves which are essentially mirror images of each other (Fig. 3b). Certain modifications of bilateral symmetry can be recognized—for example, the coiling of the shell as in snails (Fig. 3c) and structural deviations on one side of the body as in the unequal sizes of the pincers in male fiddler crabs (Fig. 3d).

Radial symmetry is found in certain animals that have the general

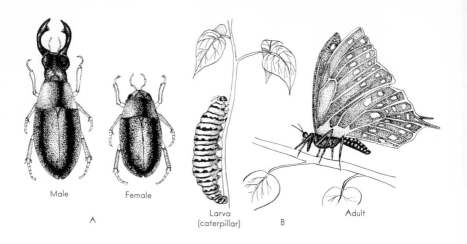

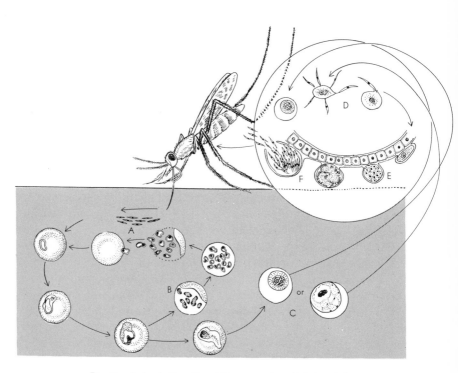

Fig. 2. Animal diversity within a species. (A) Sex differences: male and female stag beetles. (B) Developmental differences: larva and adult of Monarch butterfly. (C) Life-cycle differences: stages in the life cycle of *Plasmodium*, a parasitic protozoan which causes malaria in man.

form of a cylinder or some modification of it. Ideally, in these forms any plane that passes through the central axis of the cylinder will cut the organism into mirror halves. Actually, rarely is this ideal realized, since most so-called radially symmetrical animals have special parts, such as

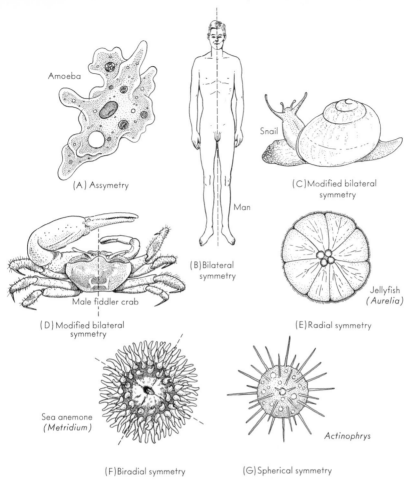

Fig. 3. Types of symmetry. (The dotted line marks the plane or planes dividing the organism into mirror halves.)

tentacles, distributed around their periphery; thus a dividing plane will achieve symmetry only if it lies precisely between two tentacles on both sides or divides a tentacle precisely in two on both sides. An example is the jellyfish (Fig. 3e).

Biradial symmetry occurs in a few animal organisms in which two planes of symmetry are present, at right angles to each other, each plane cutting the organism into mirror halves but with the mirror halves of one plane unlike those produced by the other plane. See the anemone in Fig. 3f. Finally, in *spherical symmetry,* which is found only in certain microscopic forms such as *Actinophrys* (Fig. 3g), the body is in the general shape of a sphere, and any plane passing through the center divides the body essentially into mirror halves.

These types of symmetry are idealizations, and any single organism is unlikely to be a perfect example of any of them (and remember that certain organisms are without symmetry, i.e., are asymmetrical). But in the majority of cases, we can readily tag an organism with the type of symmetry that most closely applies to it.

The variety of animal form also expresses itself in the different ways body parts are organized. We will see this most clearly later when we discuss the anatomy of various animal groups in some detail. For the present, it will be sufficient to point out that the head of a grasshopper is markedly different from that of a bird, as are the rest of their bodies, for they are organized on different plans relative to the placement of body organs. The appendages of their bodies are also quite different, and so on. Comparisons such as these between the grasshopper and the bird bring out many obvious differences. Comparisons between a beetle and a grasshopper would not reveal as many differences; nor would a comparison between a bird and a reptile.

The point to remember here is that although we will speak of heads from a variety of animals, or of ventral surfaces and oral surfaces, of legs, tails, wings, and the rest, we are referring to a great many different kinds of heads, body surfaces, legs, etc. And, most importantly, we must be prepared not only for differences but also for similarities, or, better still, for degrees of differences and similarities. This whole study of form, known as *morphology,* is of the greatest value in testing the predictions we shall soon be making.

Differences in organization are found not only in external but also in internal form. Here we will examine the placement of organ systems relative to each other and to the body as a whole. For example, the larger part of the nervous system is ventral to the digestive system in the insects, but the reverse relationship holds in animals possessing backbones, i.e., the vertebrates. This comparative approach can go into even finer detail; the structure of cells and their constituent chromosomes can be compared, but we will leave this for other volumes in the series.

Turning from structure and form, we find there is a diversity in the way different animals carry out life functions. This, of course, is not surprising, since differences in form would not only suggest but even demand different activities. Our concern here is with physiological activities, with the ways in which animals move, ingest, digest, and egest food, and so on. Differences in form and function also appear at the molecular level, although the similarities there between organisms are more striking than their differences, but this is the province of biochemistry and is taken up in another book in this series.

Animals vary also in their patterns of development. This topic, too, is dealt with elsewhere in this series, but the comparative aspects of development should be kept in mind. The vast majority of animals are capable of sexual reproduction, and follow the classic pattern of reproduction: *haploid gametes* are formed from *diploid* parents; fertilization occurs, restoring the *diploid* chromosome number, and is followed by *cleavage;* the *cleaved zygote* then goes through a number of developmental processes to achieve a new adult. Many variations, big and small, are played on this simply stated theme of sexual reproduction. And *asexual reproduction,* which is not uncommon, involves perhaps an even greater variety of processes.

Finally, we should be aware that animal diversity is expressed in the variety of habitats that animals occupy. From a close look at any cow pasture, we can see, in addition to the conspicuous cattle, many kinds of insects swarming through the grass and pestering the cows. Birds are preying on these insects, and other birds in turn are preying on the insectivorous birds. The insects, birds, and cattle are all infested with parasites, and some of the parasites even have parasites. A great variety of animals, then, lives in any single habitat, and different habitats—jungles, ocean depths, deserts, pine forests, lakes, etc.—will each contain its own diverse forms of animal life.

Conclusions

In this chapter, we have seen that there are probably at least several million distinct forms of animals, excluding minor individual variations, and that this great diversity is spread over a tremendous size range, since the largest forms are around ten million times larger than the smallest. Fortunately, we have only a few types of symmetry to apply to these forms, but when it comes to individual body parts, we are again confronted with an immense amount of variety. In addition to diversity of form, we have diversity of function, of development, and of habitat.

This enormous diversity in animals obviously requires a system to organize it into a more readily comprehensible body of information. Such a system and its application are the subject of the next chapter.

In this chapter, we will try to organize the mass of data descriptive of animal diversity. This can be done, as we shall see, by applying the methods and principles of *systematics* or *taxonomy.*

The great Swedish naturalist, Carolus Linnaeus (1707–1778), was the founder of taxonomy. This is not to say that prior to Linnaeus men had made no attempts to classify organisms, indeed the opposite is true, but earlier attempts were for the most part limited in scope and were not guided by rigorous principles that would permit broad application.

The Linnaean Binomial System

The binomial system is Linnaeus' great contribution to biology. Here for the first time animals are given two names, the first being designated the generic name and the second the specific name. That is, the first name, such as *Homo* in *Homo sapiens,* which was Linnaeus' name for man, is the name of the *genus* to which man belongs. The second name, *sapiens* in our example, is the *species* referred to within the given genus. This simple system of grouping animals into species and then genera, each identified with a unique Latin name, worked something close to a miracle in supplying man with a device by which he could effectively name different animal forms. The system, with certain refinements, is still used today.

How did Linnaeus decide what was to be a species or a genus? To begin with,

3

The Systematics of Animal Diversity

he conceived of the species as a fixed and unchanging thing. To his way of thinking, species were divinely created and persisted unchanged in the form in which they appeared. Thus a species was a group of organisms which closely resembled a given type of form. A genus was a group of species having certain characteristics in common. Linnaeus also introduced higher categories, which are still with us today: the *order*, the *class*, and the *kingdom*. Placement of the genera into orders, and orders into classes, and classes into kingdoms was done in basically the same way that species were placed into genera. The presence or absence of certain key characters determined whether organisms were placed together in one group. Animals not possessing the characters or possessing them in a different form were assigned to another group.

Since the major difference between today's systematics and that of Linnaeus lies in the concept of the species, we should first make clear what is entailed in Linnaeus' idea of the species. As we just mentioned, Linnaeus conceived of species as immutable; they simply did not change once they were created, and thus one could speak of an idealized type for each and every species. Once having described this type, Linnaeus thought the form of the species was forever secured for human knowledge. At the same time, he was always striving for a "natural system," a system that would reflect the true similarities and differences among species, genera, orders, classes, and kingdoms.

Because of his intelligent, sensitive, and imaginative mind, Linnaeus was remarkably successful in achieving a "natural system," starting from his very static type concept, but in the hands of less gifted workers, taxonomy over the years developed a reputation of sterile pigeon-holing. The Linnaean type concept led taxonomists up a blind alley and is no longer accepted; the idea that drove it out is that of biological evolution.

The Impact of Evolutionary Thought on Taxonomy

The belief that animals evolve is an old one, but it only became generally accepted through the efforts of Charles Darwin (1809–1883). In Chapter 4, Darwin and his ideas will be examined in detail; here our concern is with the effect of evolutionary theory on the type concept as described above. In brief, it destroyed the type concept, and logically so, for the central idea of evolution is change, which is the antithesis of static types.[1] According to the evolutionary theory, changes are always arising in populations of organisms in nature. Some changes will be preserved, some will die out, and some will produce even further changes. Since species are made up of natural populations, species too will change, and it becomes obvious that a Linnaean species type is a complete abstraction

[1] Today species types are still used, but in a limited way much modified from that of Linnaeus. For further discussion of this problem, see the volume by Mayr, Linsley, and Usinger listed under Selected Readings at the end of the book.

that is of little use in comprehending natural populations. Natural populations are characterized by variability, and a population is described by a sample that shows the variety existing within it. The obvious next step, then, was for taxonomists to study natural populations.

The New Systematics

The term New Systematics need imply no disrespect for the old systematics, as has been pointed out by Sir Julian Huxley, who coined the term. It simply marks a change in the development of this area of biology. The heart of the New Systematics is the replacement of the species as a stereotyped form by a description of the species as a population affected by ecological and genetic factors. The population, represented by an adequate sample, is the taxonomic unit of study. This new approach has demanded new techniques never dreamed of by Linnaeus and his followers.

The present-day systematist must recognize the statistical problems in his sampling techniques so he can judge whether his sample size is adequate or not. He must know genetics and the dynamics of the extinction or preservation of hereditary factors in a population. He must know ecology and its concern for the interaction of organism and environment and for the factors affecting the number and distribution of animals—all this in addition to being a keen observer of animal anatomy, like Linnaeus.

Today, a widely accepted definition of a species is a genetic one: a species is a group of interbreeding or potentially interbreeding populations. Such a definition, if it is testable (that is, if the organisms can be observed either to interbreed or to be incapable of interbreeding), gives a clear, objective criterion of a species, but, unfortunately, the vast majority of species are not so defined. It has been estimated that only approximately 1/10,000 of the known species are also definable as genetic species. All the rest are defined on the basis of certain structural characters.

Some biologists have suggested that the interbreeding populations or genetic species be called a syngen, with the term species left as the morphological concept, since, in some cases, the morphologist's species and the geneticist's species do not coincide. An example is the protozoan species (morphologist's sense) of *Paramecium aurelia*, in which there are at least sixteen genetic species or syngens. That is, within one group of organisms that look essentially alike, there are sixteen subgroups whose members can breed successfully only with other members of their own subgroup. Today, however, we are in the midst of this unresolved controversy. We shall use the conventional practice and apply the term species to both the genetically and the morphologically defined species.

The use of morphology, or the study of form, in describing a taxonomic category or *taxon* depends on the concept of homologous structures. Homologous structures, as discussed by the German morphologist,

Remane, are those parts of organisms that (1) are similarly placed on or within an organism, (2) are composed of subparts that are similar in form and number in different organisms, and (3) can be placed in a series such that the most dissimilar parts can be joined by a continuous array of intermediate forms. For instance, to take a well-known example, the arm of a man, the foreleg of a whale, the wing of a bat or of a bird, the foreleg of a crocodile or a frog are all homologous structures (Fig. 4). They are all similarly located on an organism; they contain similar subparts; and the extreme forms can be joined to one another by various intermediate forms found in living or fossil organisms.

That taxon which shares the greatest number of homologous structures is the species; thus a morphological definition of species is, to put it simply, a group of essentially similar living forms. A genus is a group of organisms possessing only certain homologous structures in common. A family shares even fewer homologous structures, and so on up to the highest taxa. How one decides which shared structures shall be considered as characteristic of a family rather than a genus is an arbitrary matter. Indeed, it can even be said that a good taxonomic category is what a good taxonomist says it is. This is admittedly subjective, but at the present stage of our knowledge there is no alternative. In practice it is a very useful system.

Before leaving the idea of homology, one further important point should be made clear. The concept itself is a morphological one. Why we search out homologous structures is another question; we are, in effect, asking for an explanation of them, and this is an evolutionary problem. Evolution proceeds by accumulating hereditary changes in natural populations. Small differences between two distinct populations suggest a small amount of evolutionary change from a common, ancestral popula-

Fig. 4. Homologous structures: bones of vertebrate forelimbs. (A) Forearm of man; (B) fore-flipper of a whale; (C) wing of a bat; (D) wing of a bird; (E) foreleg of a crocodile; (F) foreleg of a frog. Homologous bones are marked as follows: humerus—cross-hatched; radius—unmarked; ulna—black; carpals—heavy stippling; metacarpals and phalanges (finger bones in man)—light stippling. Numbers refer to digits (or fingers in man).

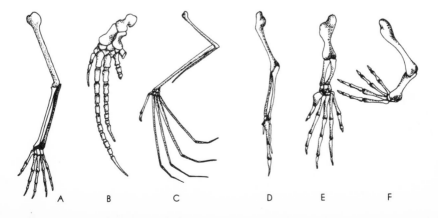

tion; large differences imply much change. The differing degrees of similarities represented by homologous structures, therefore, can reasonably be considered a measure of evolutionary change from a common progenitor. Thus the lower taxa, which show the most similarity among themselves, represent the least amount of evolutionary divergence or change from the ancestral form, and the highest taxa the greatest amount of such change. If we take several groups of organisms and diagram their relations to each other in terms of homologies, as in Fig. 5, we can get a picture of the evolutionary relations between the groups. Such a scheme is termed a phylogeny. It follows, therefore, that from homologies we can construct phylogenies.

Note that Fig. 5 is greatly simplified relative to any real situation, since a systematist would not use just a single homologous character to define the phylogenetic relations at the different taxonomic levels, but many such characters, especially at the specific and generic levels. By using many homologies, we can be more confident that these similarities do reflect descent from a common ancestral group, and are thus not the result of parallel but of independent development of similar characters, which would imply that there was no common evolutionary origin. Only when the systematist has established that his taxa are monophyletic, i.e., descended from a single ancestral group, can he construct meaningful phylogenetic schemes.

Modern biologists, then, are trying to construct a "natural classification," one which attempts to reflect the evolutionary history of a group. Linnaeus' concept of a natural classification was based on an intuitive appreciation of similarity of form. Today, ours is based on the concept of homology and its evolutionary explanation. Although our final classification is not much different from that of Linnaeus, our appreciation of what is meant by the term natural classification is indeed quite different.

TAXA

Before proceeding, we should clarify certain terms regarding taxonomic categories. Some of these we have already discussed, e.g., species. Others we have touched on more briefly, such as the Linnaean terms of genus, order, class, and kingdom. To these terms we have added two more since Linnaeus' day: family and phylum. Here are our present taxonomic categories, starting with species and proceeding in sequence on up to kingdom.

Species (same form for both singular and plural)
Genus (plural: genera)
Family
Order
Class
Phylum (plural: phyla)
Kingdom

Step 1:   DESCRIPTION of the distribution of homolgies among various natural populations or groups of populations.

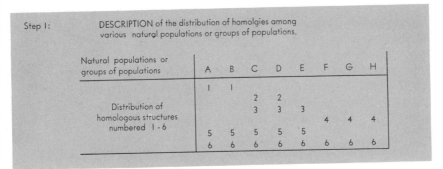

Natural populations or groups of populations	A	B	C	D	E	F	G	H
Distribution of homologous structures numbered 1 - 6	1	1						
			2	2				
			3	3	3			
						4	4	4
	5	5	5	5	5			
	6	6	6	6	6	6	6	6

Step 2:   GROUPINGS on the basis of homologous structures.

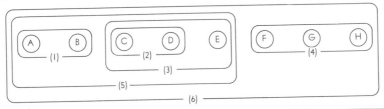

Step 3:   PLACEMENT of groups in taxa.

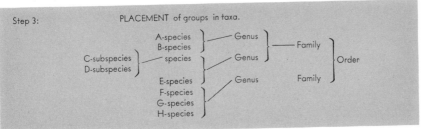

Step 4:   FORMULATION of phylogenetic relations.

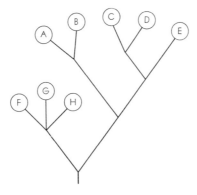

Fig. 5. A diagram illustrating the use of homologies to determine phylogenetic relations.

These categories or taxa (singular: taxon) are often broken into smaller groups, not only by going to the next lower taxon, but also by adding the prefix, sub-, to the taxon that is being so subdivided. For example, a suborder is a group within an order, and would contain within it one or more families. Occasionally, the prefix, super-, is used. A superfamily, for example, is a taxon containing one or more families and is itself contained within a suborder or order, which is the next higher taxon.

Finally, we must describe certain conventions regarding taxonomic terms. First, a species name is always italicized, and the first letter of the generic name is capitalized. Example: *Homo sapiens*. Second, whenever just the genus is being referred to, the generic name is again italicized and capitalized. Exceptions to these rules occur when there is no good English or other common name for the organism and the generic name has come to be used as a common name. An example is amoeba; here both italics and the capital are omitted. Third, the name of any taxon other than the species always has the first letter capitalized, as in Vertebrata, or Insecta, but when these terms are anglicized, the capitals are omitted and Vertebrata becomes vertebrates, Insecta becomes insects. Figure 6 shows the classification of three well-known animals.

Figure 6

Systematics of the dog, the wolf, and the honeybee.

	Dog	*Wolf*	*Honeybee*
Kingdom	Animalia	Animalia	Animalia
Phylum	Chordata	Chordata	Arthropoda
Subphylum	Vertebrata	Vertebrata	
Class	Mammalia	Mammalia	Insecta
Order	Carnivora	Carnivora	Hymenoptera
Family	Canidae	Canidae	Apidae
Genus	*Canis*	*Canis*	*Apis*
Species	*domesticus*	*lupus*	*mellifera*

To summarize, then, taxonomy today is in a new and vigorous period. The contemporary systematist is trained in many biological disciplines. His goal is still the Linnaean "natural system," but defined now with evolution in the back of his mind. His unit of study is no longer a static abstraction but a natural population; his analysis is performed on a dynamic entity. The problem of a species definition is solved genetically, but in practice most species are defined not by genetic but by morphological studies.

THE MAJOR ANIMAL PHYLA

In the preceding chapter, we emphasized how great is the diversity of animals. In this chapter, we have stated that taxonomy supplies a technique for comprehending this diversity. We now wish to see just how animals can be grouped into a taxonomic system. In this section, we shall confine ourselves to brief statements concerning the major characteristics of eight of the largest phyla in the animal kingdom. Later on we shall have to amplify these descriptions and to introduce more phyla.

Let us start with the phylum to which man belongs, Chordata. One of the most important characters common to all members of this taxon is the presence of a rod, called the notochord, along the back or dorsal side, at least in the young forms. In many forms, this notochord is lost in the adults and is replaced by a jointed structure called the backbone. Forms bearing a backbone are the vertebrates. In addition to possessing the dorsal rod, the chordates are bilaterally symmetrical, and most possess a well-developed tail. The trunk, the rest of the body between the head and tail, contains well-developed organ systems and often has locomotory appendages. Fishes, frogs, lizards (see Fig. 7), birds, and mammals are all chordates. Altogether this phylum contains approximately 40,000 described species.

Our next phylum contains more species than those in all the rest of the living world combined, mainly because this group, the Arthropoda, includes the insects. Indeed the insects alone, with some 800,000 described species, represent well over half the known species of living things. The arthropods are distinguished by the presence of a hard, outer skeleton or exoskeleton. The body is bilaterally symmetrical and is *segmented*, that is, subdivisible at right angles to the long axis of the body into roughly similar parts. In some forms, such as crabs, however, this segmentation is not at all obvious to the untrained eye. The body contains well-developed

Fig. 7. Selected chordates. (A) A cutaway view of a tunicate larva, showing chordate characters (redrawn from Buchsbaum). (B) *Antennarius chironectes,* an angler fish. (C) The grass frog, *Rana pipiens,* an amphibian. (D) The garter snake.

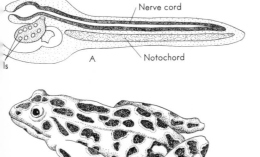

Nerve cord

A

Notochord

ls

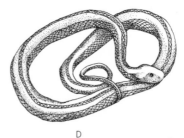

C

D

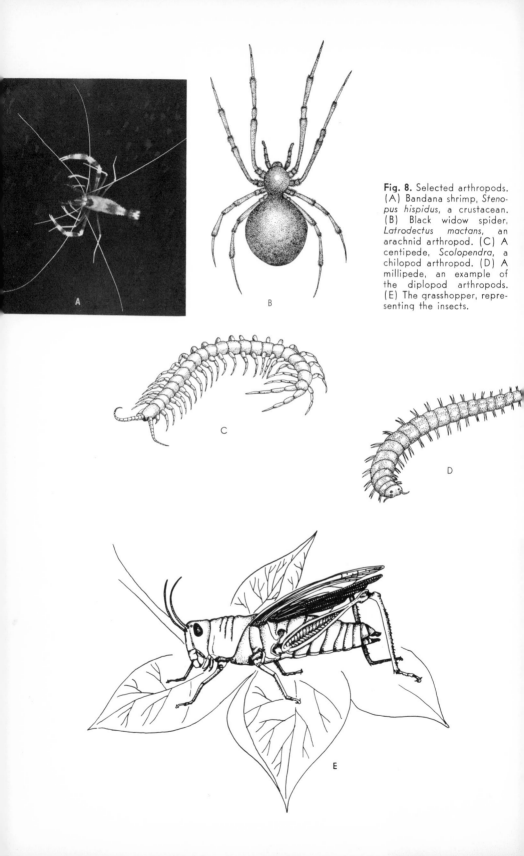

Fig. 8. Selected arthropods. (A) Bandana shrimp, *Stenopus hispidus,* a crustacean. (B) Black widow spider, *Latrodectus mactans,* an arachnid arthropod. (C) A centipede, *Scolopendra,* a chilopod arthropod. (D) A millipede, an example of the diplopod arthropods. (E) The grasshopper, representing the insects.

organs. The appendages, such as the legs and antennae, are jointed (in fact, the name *arthro-poda* means jointed feet). These organisms are found almost the world over, in water, on land, and in the air; from ocean depths to mountain heights; from rain forest to desert; from hot to cold climates. Examples of arthropods are shown in Fig. 8. All arthropod groups combined contain over 900,000 species.

Another group of bilaterally symmetrical and segmented forms is that of the Annelida. They, too, have appendages but these are not jointed. Their soft bodies are typically worm-like in form. Their internal organs are well developed, and the segmentation of the body is clear in both the external and internal body parts. They are found in oceans and fresh water, usually dwelling on the bottom, and on land. Earthworms are an example of the group. Clam worms, with their conspicuous appendages, are perhaps an even better example; they are found along our East and West Coasts. There are around 7,000 described species of annelids (Fig. 9).

In the Mollusca, which is primarily an aquatic phylum (only the snails live on land in any numbers), the body contains well-developed organ systems and is bilaterally symmetrical, or has a modified bilaterality as in snails. Most of them have a hard shell-like structure; clams have two valves, as the shells are called, and snails have a shell, but in octopuses and squids the shell is an internal structure reduced in size or missing completely. Segmentation is present only in one small subgroup, the

Fig. 9. Selected annelids. (A) *Eunice interrupta*, a polychete worm. (B) *Lumbricus*, the common earthworm. (C) *Hirudo medicinalis*, a leech.

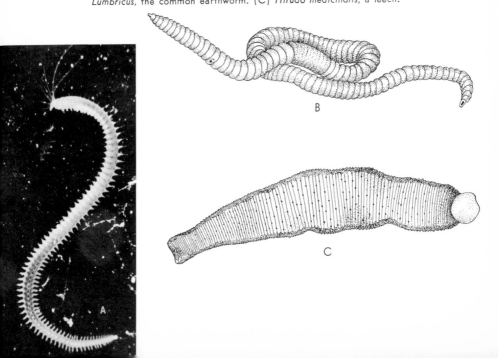

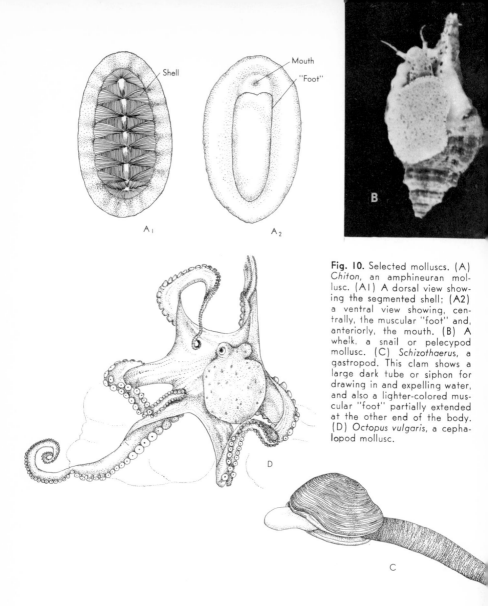

Shell

Mouth

"Foot"

A₁

A₂

B

Fig. 10. Selected molluscs. (A) *Chiton*, an amphineuran mollusc. (A1) A dorsal view showing the segmented shell; (A2) a ventral view showing, centrally, the muscular "foot" and, anteriorly, the mouth. (B) A whelk, a snail or pelecypod mollusc. (C) *Schizothaerus*, a gastropod. This clam shows a large dark tube or siphon for drawing in and expelling water, and also a lighter-colored muscular "foot" partially extended at the other end of the body. (D) *Octopus vulgaris*, a cephalopod mollusc.

D

C

chitons. This assemblage of clams, snails, and octopuses (see Fig. 10) is a large one and, because of their shells, has left an excellent fossil record. Known species number approximately 80,000.

Another exclusively aquatic phylum, the Echinodermata, occurs only in salt water, and its members, such as the starfish, have a kind of radial symmetry, with five similar parts radiating from a central axis. Actually, as larvae, the echinoderms are bilaterally symmetrical; only as they develop into adults does their typical pentaradiate form appear. Their body organs are well developed. Their name, meaning spiny-skinned, is especially appropriate for such members of the group as the pincushion-like sea urchins (see Fig. 11). There are over 4,000 species in this group, which is also well represented as fossils.

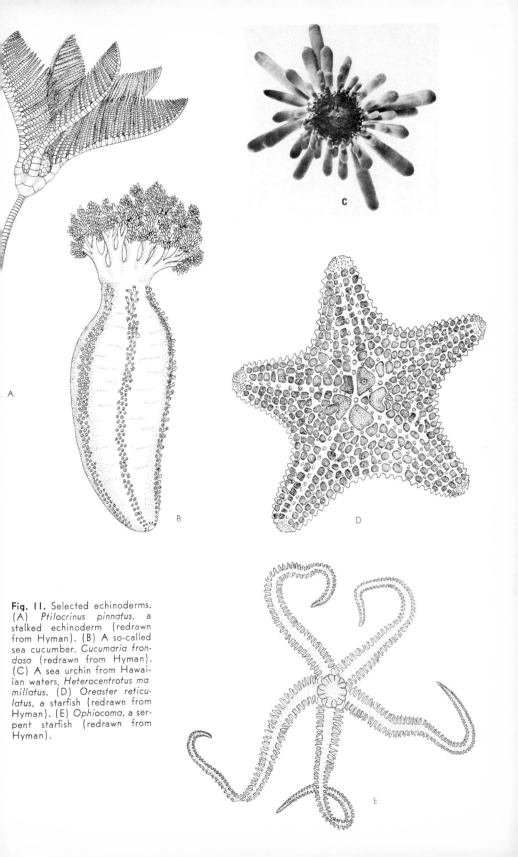

Fig. 11. Selected echinoderms. (A) *Ptilocrinus pinnatus*, a stalked echinoderm (redrawn from Hyman). (B) A so-called sea cucumber, *Cucumaria frondosa* (redrawn from Hyman). (C) A sea urchin from Hawaiian waters, *Heterocentrotus mamillatus*. (D) *Oreaster reticulatus*, a starfish (redrawn from Hyman). (E) *Ophiocoma*, a serpent starfish (redrawn from Hyman).

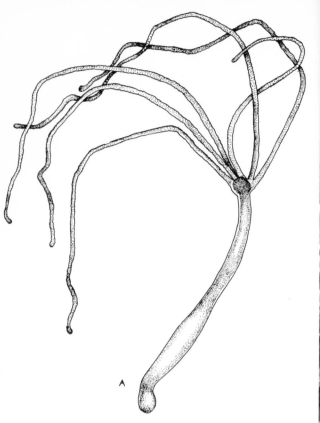

Fig. 12. Selected cnidarians. (A) *Hydra littoralis,* a common hydrozoan polyp. (B) *Rhizostomum oscillatum,* a scyphozoan medusa. (C) *Baloceroides lilae,* an oral view of an anthozoan polyp, showing its biradial symmetry.

The phylum Cnidaria, or coelenterates as they are commonly called, is the only other one of these eight that possesses radial symmetry. Certain members of the group are biradial. In contrast to the preceding five phyla, the internal organs of the group are not very complex. For example, there is only one opening to the digestive cavity, and it must serve for both ingestion and egestion. The cnidarians are aquatic, being predominantly marine forms. The best-known forms are jellyfish (see Fig. 12) and the animals that produce corals. They all possess tentacles, which carry characteristic stinging cells. About 9,000 species are described.

The Platyhelminthes or flatworms contain a wide variety of forms. These are bilaterally symmetrical, but, like the coelenterates, they show little differentiation of internal organs compared to the first five phyla we have mentioned. Many of the flatworms are parasitic and have assumed rather bizarre forms. Those that are free-living are mostly aquatic and,

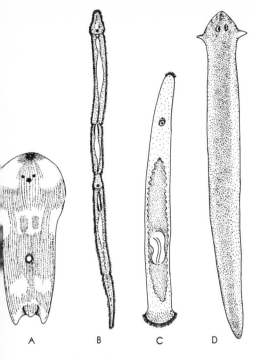

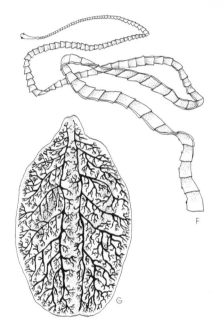

Fig. 13. Selected flatworms. (A) *Amphiscolops bermudensis*, a free-living, acoelous flatworm (redrawn from Hyman). (B) *Catenula lemnae*, a free-living rhabdocoelous flatworm (redrawn from Hyman). (C) *Monocelis*, an alleocoelous flatworm, also free-living (redrawn from Hyman). (D) *Dugesia dorotocephala*, a free-living planarian triclad flatworm (redrawn from Hyman). (E) *Descodelus insularis*, a free-living marine polyclad flatworm (courtesy Dr. Sidney J. Townsley, University of Hawaii). (F) *Taenia saginata*, the parasitic beef tapeworm (redrawn from Buchsbaum). (G) *Fasciola hepatica*, a parasitic sheep liver fluke, showing the highly branched digestive cavity.

being small, are not commonly seen. Planaria (see Fig. 13) is the best known of the free-living forms; the beef tapeworm and liver fluke are examples of the parastic forms. There are roughly 6,000 described species.

The last group to be considered is the Protozoa, a heterogeneous group whose diversity of form mirrors the wide variety of habitats occupied by its members. No other group is as widespread, largely because hardly a group of animals exists which is not parasitized by one or more kinds of protozoan. The free-living forms are also world-wide in their distribution. The Protozoa show all kinds of symmetry (Fig. 14). Their bodies are not divided into cells as are the bodies of all the other animal phyla. In this sense, these organisms are called acellular, as compared to the cellular organisms we have already mentioned. Since the body of the protozoan is made up of a bounding membrane, which encloses cytoplasm and nucleus, however, it possesses the major structural features of a cell. For this reason, the Protozoa are more commonly called unicellular, as

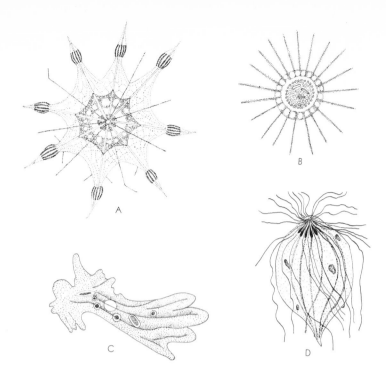

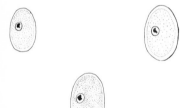

Fig. 14. Selected protozoans. (A) *Acanthometra pellucida*, a free-living marine radiolarian (redrawn from Hall). (B) *Actinospherium eichorni*, an actinopodan from fresh water (redrawn from Hall). (C) *Amoeba proteus*, the common amoeba from fresh water (redrawn from Hall). (D) *Coronympha clevelandi*, a parasitic form with flagella (redrawn from Hall). (E) *Nosema elongatum*, the spore of a parasitic microsporidian (redrawn from Hall). (F) *Paramecium aurelia*, a free-living ciliated protozoan in the process of transverse fission (see also Fig. 37).

compared to the rest of the animals, which are termed multicellular. A final choice between these two sets of terms has not been made; most people prefer unicellular and multicellular, but in this book we shall use acellular and cellular, since they more accurately describe the difference in organization between protozoan organisms and other animals. There are at least 30,000 described species of protozoans, most of which are so tiny (such as the Microsporida) as to be microscopic.

By discussing animal diversity in this fashion, we have been able to divide roughly 1,100,000 animals into eight major groups. Using our previous estimate of at least 1,200,000 described species, we can see that our system will cover more than 90 per cent of the known species. The remaining 10 per cent are covered by other phyla, some of which we will examine later.

POSTSCRIPT ON SYSTEMATICS

Even though man has come this far in cataloging the diversity of animals, much remains to be done. For example, in 1933 Remane carefully examined the microscopic marine animal life of a part of north Germany that had already been extensively studied. In ten years, he found 300 new species, which included members of 15 new families. Many animal groups are poorly known—for example, certain of the flatworm groups. Others are well known, such as birds—for example, very few new North American bird species are ever discovered any more.

Comments and Conclusions

Now that we have completed our preliminary description of animal diversity, the following points emerge. Despite a great variety of differences, certain forms possess homologous structures that are either modified or absent in other forms. By grouping together animals that possess certain homologous features in common, we find that the several million animal forms can be classified into a small number of easily characterized groups. Such groups we call phyla, and within phyla we can organize the members into further groups by examining other sets of homologous characters. Progressing in this way, we find that all animals can be placed in a system of classification which quite precisely defines their degree of similarity, or, conversely, their degree of difference, to all other animals.

What does this mean? How can we explain the fact that man can so organize his experience of animal diversity that all known animals can be grouped to express varying degrees of similarity, or difference, in form based on homologies? This question is the formulation of the problem in our attempt to understand animal diversity.

4

Darwin

and

The Origin

of

Species

Man's curiosity about the great variety of living forms is responsible for the idea of evolution. Scientists, ever since Aristotle, have been attempting to explain animal diversity in terms of evolution. But what do we mean by evolution? The most convincing answer to that question is attributed to Charles Darwin and will be examined in this chapter. The purpose of this chapter is threefold: to investigate what factors led Darwin to believe in evolution; to describe his theory, which attempts to explain evolution; and to point out briefly why this theory was so revolutionary, not only to biologists, but also to the intellectual history of mankind.

Voyage of the H.M.S. *Beagle*

In the same year that he graduated from Cambridge, 1831, Darwin signed on, at the age of 22, as the naturalist for the voyage of the ship, H.M.S. *Beagle*, which was to circumnavigate the world mainly for map-making purposes. Darwin's job was to collect rocks, plants, and animals from the various places visited along the route. He worked energetically and thoroughly, when on land, but at sea he was continuously seasick. This seasickness eventually affected his constitution, and his very bad health in later life has been attributed, at least in part, to this buffeting received by his system. The trip gave Darwin his real training as a scientist and shaped the direction of his entire future. In his autobiography, he himself wrote: "The voyage of the Beagle has been by far the most important event in my life, and has determined my whole career. . . ." Upon returning to England, he spent the next years writing reports on the objects he had collected, and it was during this period that the glimmerings of a new understanding of the diversity of life first sparked in his mind.

Before turning to his theory, we should briefly examine the type of material Darwin was poring over. The material can be divided into two categories: fossils and zoogeographic data (data concerning the distribution of animals). Darwin discovered great fossil beds in Argentina (we are still studying them today), and he was much impressed by certain fossil animals there that showed armor much like that covering the existing armadillos (Fig. 15). In other words, obvious similarities were visible

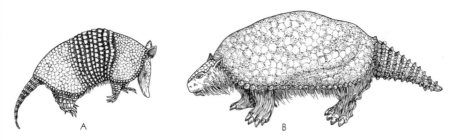

Fig. 15. South American armadillos. (A) Nine-banded armadillo of today. (B) Extinct glyptodon, reconstructed from fossils.

between forms which had lived in the distant past and forms living in his day. Regarding zoogeography, Darwin observed that the same form of a certain animal was not found over the whole of South America. Rather, he noticed that similar forms replaced one another as one proceeded southwards on the continent. That is, as one form of the animal became rare, moving southwards, another similar but distinctly different one appeared in the haunts where one might have expected the first. Farther south, the second form might be replaced by a third, and so on.

The most intriguing puzzles in animal distribution came when the *Beagle* and its naturalist visited the Galapagos Islands, some 600 miles west of Ecuador. The fauna of these isolated islands was for the most part distinctly South American in character, although it differed somewhat from island to island. Darwin puzzled a great deal over these differences, and over the fact that these animals were South American-like, but yet different. "It was evident," he noted in his autobiography, "that such facts as these, as well as many others, could only be explained on the supposition that species gradually become modified; and the subject haunted me."

But how to explain this gradual modification? If there was no good explanation for the gradual changes, it would be very difficult to accept the idea of change, especially since the prevailing doctrine was, as Linnaeus had announced, that species were immutable. Darwin started collecting facts bearing on this possibility of change in 1837. After much diligent compilation of data and the writing of a 35-page "very brief abstract" in 1842, to which he added 230 pages in 1844, he wrote to his friend Hooker, a distinguished British botanist, "I have read heaps of agricultural books and have never ceased collecting facts. At last gleams of light have come, and I am almost convinced (quite contrary to the opinion I started with) that species are not (it is like confessing a murder) immutable."

Natural Selection

In his letter to Hooker, Darwin is probably understating his position when he says, ". . . I am almost convinced . . .," for in 1838 he had read Malthus' *Essay on Population* and this had supplied him the key insight he needed to explain his postulated mutability of species. Malthus' theme in this famous treatise stressed that whereas the food supply increases arithmetically, populations increase geometrically. The result, as Darwin saw it, would be a great struggle for existence, and his long experience as a naturalist gave him first-hand knowledge of this struggle as it is waged in nature; ". . . it at once struck me that under these circumstances favourable variations would tend to be preserved, and unfavourable ones to be destroyed" (from the autobiography).

What Charles Darwin now clearly perceived was that if any organism had an advantage over its neighbor in obtaining or using things necessary for life, that organism would be the one most likely to survive. If this advantageous character were inherited by future generations and thereby they were insured of a greater chance of survival than those organisms lacking this character, forms with the advantageous character eventually would predominate in the population. And in this population the organism with a new advantageous variation would be the one most likely to succeed. Thus changes would accumulate through the passage of generations. In some areas, one type of change would be more advantageous than another, although it could be disadvantageous in a different area. If this occurred, two populations would emerge that differed in the presence or absence of the characters in question. Darwin called this process *natural selection*.

More precisely stated, Darwin's explanation for change in organisms consists of three inductive generalizations and two deductions. The *first induction* is that natural populations are capable of an enormous and rapid increase in numbers. This is easily illustrated: a single cod can lay over 6,000,000 eggs; an oak tree, grown from a single acorn, produces hundreds of new acorns year after year; and if we assume the average married couple in humans has four children who in their turn grow up and marry, the human population will double in a generation and increase a millionfold in 20 generations if there is 100 per cent survival to maturity. The *second induction* is that, for the most part, natural populations do not increase in number, but remain relatively constant in size. The oceans are not choked with cod; the woods not filled with oaks; humans, it is true, are increasing geometrically in number, but they represent an understandable exception.

The *first deduction* now follows: since there is a potentiality for an enormous increase in number and this is not realized, there must be a struggle for existence going on which keeps the numbers of natural populations fairly constant. The *third induction* is that variations appear in nature, and some of these are heritable. New strains of wheat, new color patterns in flowers, and a larger size in this or that organism are all possible examples of heritable variations. The *second deduction* follows from the first deduction and the third inductive generalization: if heritable variations occur in the midst of the struggle for existence, those organisms possessing variations which increase their chance of survival are the ones that will persist. That is, natural selection will occur.

Darwin's first public presentation of the theory of the origin of species by natural selection occurred in 1858. At a meeting of the Linnaean Society in London, a paper by Darwin and a paper by Alfred Russel Wallace were read, *both* proposing natural selection as the means by which organisms evolve. Wallace, it is interesting to note, like Darwin, was a naturalist, a student of zoogeography in an archipelago (that of the East Indies), and had also read Malthus! Indeed, Wallace testifies that the essay on population had a revelatory effect on him, an effect remarkably similar to its impact on Darwin.

How these two men arrived independently at the same great idea is explained by the fact that both were men of similar background in biology and they were working on the same kind of problem. They both also happened to read the same key discussion of population problems. Beyond this, we cannot say why some men come up with a fruitful hypothesis, and others do not. We do know that Darwin and Wallace, independently, formulated the same hypothesis of natural selection. Darwin had been working on the idea longer than Wallace and unquestionably possessed a more profound insight into it. Within thirteen months of the meeting of the Linnaean Society, Darwin brought his extensive notes together and published his great book, *The Origin of Species,* which sold out the first edition on the day it was offered for sale.

Although it would be fascinating and profitable to examine the evidence which tests the hypothesis of natural selection, from the publication of *The Origin of Species* down to the present day, and evidence has been collected which supports the hypothesis, we cannot take the time to study this evidence here (see the book on adaptation in this series).[1] We will simply conclude that the hypothesis is acceptable and point out its bearing on what we understand by the concept of evolution.

We must now introduce the idea of adaptation. Adaptation is the fitting of an organism to its environment so as to insure its continued survival and reproduction. The word is also used in another sense. It can refer to a character of an organism that helps it survive in its environment. For instance, the webbed foot of a duck is an adaptation for swimming. Our concern here, however, is with adaptation in the broad sense, with the adjustments the whole organism makes to its environment in order to live and reproduce.

Since natural selection preserves the best-adapted organisms, those organisms which possess heritable variations of an advantageous character are the ones that persist. This is another way of saying that the organisms best adapted to their habitats are the ones that survive. We can thus conclude that natural selection maintains a continual pressure on natural populations to preserve the best-adapted members of the population. From this, we can define evolution as follows: *Evolution is the sum total of adaptive changes preserved by natural selection.*

A Turning Point in Biological Thought

The concept of evolution is the most important generalization in biology. It ranks with Galileo's contributions to mechanics, Newton's theory of gravitation, and the modern theory of the atom. There is hardly an area of human thought not affected by it. Darwin not only made the concept acceptable by giving us a reasonable explanation of why evolution should be expected in nature—because of the unceasing action of natural selection—but in *The Origin of Species* he masterfully presented evidence in support of his hypothesis and even effectively anticipated many of the criticisms later raised against his theory. Today, most of us accept evolution as part of our outlook on the world, and we are learning that not only have living things evolved, but so has our world, our solar system, our galaxy, and our whole universe, although, of course, not in the same manner as living things.

Apart from what it contributed to our view of nature, Darwin's theory is important because it represents a new way of thinking in biology. We can probably best see this by comparing Darwin with Lamarck (1744–

---

[1] B. Wallace and A. M. Srb, *Adaptation* (Englewood Cliffs, N.J.: Prentice-Hall, 1961).

1829), who also was an outstanding proponent of evolution. In Lamarck's view, organisms change because of two factors. First, an inner plastic force in all living nature is forever driving toward a more perfect organization. Second, the environment tends to obstruct this drive towards an ideal state. In responding to the disturbances from the environment, the organism develops a simple response into a change in behavior, a change in behavior into a habit, a habit into a change in organs and ultimately into a change in general organization. This last change is presumably heritable. Use and disuse thus lead to heritable change as a part of the perfecting principle inherent in each and every organism, and this process ended in what Lamarck termed the inheritance of acquired characters. To Lamarck, then, observed changes were an expression of the action of self-perfecting life in the face of insensible, inorganic nature. He was the last great biologist to express this subjective, almost poetic, view of life.

Darwin's handling of observed changes or heritable variations was completely different from Lamarck's. Where Lamarck could not see change except as an inherent part of the whole organism, Darwin could deal with variation as a concept divorced from organisms. Darwin accepted variation as a fact, even though he had no explanation for it. Such a position was impossible for Lamarck. This ability to objectify nature, to break up nature into concepts which are rationally manipulated as objects, distinguishes Darwin from Lamarck. As one historian of science has recently said, "So far as the intellectual and cultural significance of evolutionary theory is concerned, therefore, Darwin had no predecessor in Lamarck. Lamarck's theory of evolution belongs to the contracting and self-defeating history of subjective science, and Darwin's to the expanding and conquering history of objective science."

Conclusions

We should leave this chapter with the following main ideas: After long first-hand observation and study, Darwin realized that species are not immutable. His next problem was to develop an explanation for change in species, and he solved it by formulating his theory of natural selection. It states that in the struggle for survival, which occurs in nature as the result of an enormous reproductive potential acting within a limited environment, those organisms will persist which have gained an advantage through some new, adaptively significant, heritable variation. By accumulating such variations in many successive generations, living forms will gradually change. The sum total of such adaptive changes in living things is called evolution. *The Origin of Species* was a detailed compilation of evidence in favor of the theory of natural selection. Widespread acceptance of the theory has led to general acceptance of the concept of evolution, and we now think of all living things as having evolved.

5

Evolution
and
Animal
Diversity

In the first chapter, we said that an explanatory hypothesis attempts to relate an unresolved problem to other, already accepted, statements. We now face the task of demonstrating how evolution explains animal diversity. That is, we must show how animal diversity can be understood in terms of evolution and its related concepts and facts. This is the first aim of this chapter. The second is to derive predictions that follow from this explanatory hypothesis.

Let us begin by recalling the formulation of our problem regarding animal diversity. Can we explain why man can organize his knowledge of animal form so that all known animals are systematically grouped according to their degrees of similarity based on homologies? Recall also our definition of evolution as the sum total of adaptive changes preserved by natural selection. How does this definition help explain our question?

First let us examine the idea of biological reproduction. All organisms reproduce, and this fact is inherent in the first generalization Darwin used to derive his theory of natural selection. Implicit in the idea of reproduction are two points: (1) present-day organisms always come from pre-existing organisms, and (2) offspring resemble their parents (the offspring of dogs are dogs, not cats; indeed, the offspring of poodles are poodles, not collies). Both these points have a bearing on the problem of animal diversity. Notice that in the first point we said "*present*-day organisms always come from pre-existing organisms." This means that spontaneous generation does not occur.

Spontaneous generation, it should be noted, is not the same thing as the original origin of life, or *biopoiesis,* as it is termed. Biopoiesis is limited to the origin of the first system that can be called living, and that system probably had little resemblance, at least in form, to our present organisms and was much simpler than anything living today. Spontaneous generation, then, and not biopoiesis, refers to the question of whether present-day forms can arise complete in all details from nonlife. Although there are many excellent reasons for concluding that biopoiesis occurred, we do not think it could take place today, because it would require the presence in nature of a high concentration of complex organic compounds that we know could not exist now for any length of time because bacteria and other microorganisms would promptly consume them. Biopoiesis could occur only in a world where such forms were absent, in a sterile world, and such a world has long since vanished.

Although biopoiesis cannot take place today (except perhaps in a laboratory!), the presence of life on this earth argues that it did occur at least once in the history of our planet. If life only originated at one time and place, then all living things trace their ancestry, ultimately, back to one common ancestor. We have no way at present, however, to determine whether there was only one progenitor or several. The basic similarities of metabolic patterns and subcellular morphology in organisms suggest a fundamental unity of all life, and hence possibly a common ancestor. In any case, well before the first animals appeared on earth the possibility of further origins of life was probably ended, for at that time forms which we would probably recognize as bacteria and algae—and fungi, too, perhaps—were the predominant ones. Since no more biopoiesis occurred, animals must have arisen from these early organisms, and all contemporary forms must be the evolved offspring of these earlier forms. In brief, animals may have had one common ancestor or they may have had several (we shall have occasion to discuss this problem later), and there is at least one line of common evolutionary descent for all living things, although there may be more. If we combine this conclusion with our second point, i.e., the similarity of offspring and parents, we can see why similarities exist among living things—animals included, of course. This, then, raises the next question: Where do the differences come from?

The preservation of heritable variations by natural selection supplies a possible explanation of differences in form among animals. Here we relate the well-known facts of heredity to our problem of animal diversity through the concept of natural selection. Not only can we see how natural selection could achieve successive changes in a single population, but we can see how two or more diverging lines of evolution could arise from a single population. This would occur when certain members of a population became adapted to one mode of life in an isolated locale, while the rest of the population adjusted to a different environment. In time, this initial divergence might widen considerably, perhaps to the extent that the original divergent lines would branch into distinctly different populations. The members of the most recently diverged populations, therefore, would still be quite similar to one another, but very different from descendants of the populations which diverged many generations previously. The preservation of heritable variations by natural selection would thus explain not only the differences among animals, but also degrees of difference, or conversely, degrees of similarity. And this is just what we need to understand our formulation of the problem of animal diversity.

In short, we can now state our working hypothesis in this way: *Animal diversity can be systematically arranged into groups of animals that show differing degrees of similarity based on homology, because all animals have evolved—that is, they have passed through successive generations (probably starting from one or at most a few ancestral forms) in which adaptive changes have been preserved by natural selection.*

Predictions

The predictions we can now make fall into three groups. The first concerns what will be called diversity in time; the second, diversity in space; and the third, phylogeny.

DIVERSITY IN TIME

Diversity in time refers to those changes that have occurred in the past history of an animal group. To study these changes, we must, of course, know what animals, now long dead, were like many, many years ago. Fossils supply us with this knowledge. Once we have unearthed the fossils, what should we expect to find?

First, we should expect changes, but of a certain kind. Darwin, looking at the Patagonian fossils, inferred correctly that species are not immutable, but when he used the theory of natural selection to explain how these changes came about he had to conclude they were all most likely small digressions produced by what we know today as gene mutations. In the fossil record, then, we should look for only slight differences in successive animal forms.

Second, we should expect to see a direction in the change. The older forms should be less complex than today's forms, for we have no reason to suppose that complex biological systems can be built up any other way than by starting from simpler structures and becoming more complex.

Third, since we know from the study of rocks that the earth's climate and its mountains, plains, rivers, and seas have been continually altered, we can expect to find that habitats also have been changing. Some forms will die out if their habitat changes and they cannot evolve as fast as other forms to take over new habitats. These forms thus become extinct, and their place is taken by forms that will be quite different from the progenitors shared by them both. If forms with different ancestors come to occupy a similar habitat, they might evolve somewhat similar forms as they adapt to the same environmental problems.

Our predictions regarding temporal diversity, then, can be summed up in this way: (1) change results from the accumulation of many small differences; (2) the changes go from simpler to more complex forms; and (3) forms become extinct, new forms emerge and diverge from their ancestors and among themselves, and some forms perhaps even converge.

DIVERSITY IN SPACE

By *spatial diversity* we mean the distribution of animals in space, i.e., throughout the habitable areas of the earth. Spatial diversity, of course, exists today. From our understanding of evolution, what should we expect this diversity to be like? The most obvious expectation is for all forms to be specially adapted to their way of life. We have already touched on this problem, and its analysis is intimately connected with demonstrating the actual occurrence of natural selection. Here, as before, we will assume that natural selection occurs and that all organisms are adapted to some extent. Our question now is: What kind of diversity should we expect of animals that have undergone adaptive changes? *First,* since each natural population represents the exploitation of a given way of life or *niche* over a period of many generations, we should predict that different animal forms exploit different niches. That is, different kinds of animals will not pursue the same mode of life, although similar forms will probably have similar niches.

Second, we should expect the fauna of a broad geographical area to have many forms peculiar to that area. That is, certain forms will characterize one area and will be found only in that area, because as the forms increasingly exploit the niches of that area they will evolve forms not found elsewhere, since (1) this niche might not be present anywhere else, and (2) even if it were, it might be filled by some other group. But we need to define more precisely what we mean by "broad geographical area." The kind of area we have in mind is one that is clearly set off from its neighbors into a natural unit—the continents are good examples. We would say, then, that the continents have their own peculiar fauna, even though we know that flying animals are not greatly impeded by water barriers. Restricting our prediction to mammals, which, except for bats and a few aquatic forms, are land-bound, we could say: The various continental land masses will have their own characteristic mammalian fauna.

Third, and as a corollary to the second prediction, we should expect a given mode of life to be exploitable by quite different kinds of organisms. This follows from our previous knowledge that similar habitats can be geographically isolated and hence not necessarily invaded or exploited by forms from the same taxon, perhaps simply because that taxon might not be present in both areas.

In summary, our three possible predictions are: (1) each animal form represents a separate way of life; (2) distinct geographical areas, such as continents, will have distinct and characteristic faunas; and (3) a given way of life occurring in separate geographical areas can be exploited by forms from different taxa.

PHYLOGENY

The third and final area of prediction is that of *phylogeny.* Phylogeny, as we saw earlier, is the attempt to reconstruct the course of evolution through the application of systematics. Our prediction is this: From a systematic study of the animal groups, we should be able to arrange them in a sequence of forms that will represent a plausible scheme of evolutionary change, i.e., a phylogeny. We predict this because evolution is a historical process that progresses by successive changes in living forms. New forms differ only slightly from their immediate ancestors because there are only so many ways a given organism can vary and still survive, although over a long period of time the accumulated variations can result in a great difference between the evolved and the ancestral form. Even then, however, certain basic patterns of organization will still probably persist, and, in addition, many of the transitional forms might still be alive or only slightly changed or preserved as fossils. As we said in Chapter 3, the ultimate aim of systematics is to classify organisms in a scheme that will bring out their evolutionary relationships. We must now test our predictions to see if we can arrange the taxa in such a way as to represent a plausible sequence of evolutionary change, and in the process we may also come closer to determining whether animals arose from one ancestor or from several.

Conclusions

We have now completed the second step in our attempt to apply a scientific methodology to the problem of understanding animal diversity. Evolution, as defined in Darwinian terms, is our explanatory hypothesis. From it we have derived predictions regarding diversity in time and space and regarding phylogeny. We turn to the next step, which is the testing of our predictions.

6

Temporal Diversity: Paleontology

In testing our predictions, we must examine the fossil history of animals to determine (1) whether there has been change as a result of the accumulation of many small changes, (2) whether the change has been from simpler to more complex forms, and (3) whether there is evidence of extinction of old forms, of emergence of new forms, of divergence of closely related forms, and of convergence of somewhat distantly related forms.

Fossils

Before we check the predictions, however, we must know just what fossils and the fossil record are. A *fossil* is any evidence of life in the geological past. This definition is broader than the one we commonly apply to animal fossils, for we usually refer simply to the bones, teeth, or shells of long-dead forms. But footprints also can be logically considered as fossils, as in the case of dinosaur tracks, and so can the trails of worms left on the bottom mud of bygone seas. The impressions of soft-bodied animals, such as jellyfish, in mud which later hardens into rock are also fossils. Whole mammoths have been preserved in frozen arctic bogs—in what amounts to a polar deep-freeze—and they are unique and enlightening fossils. Giant sloths have been found in a dried-out condition in Patagonian caves; large parts of the animals' dried skin and hair, tendons, and

37

dried excrement have been discovered with the bones. Fossil remains of this sort are extraordinarily rare and, although interesting, do not contribute much to the total picture of past life. At least 99 per cent of our known animal fossils consist of preserved hard parts, and it is from these that we obtain the bulk of our information regarding the life of the past.

Fossilization of a dead organism or its parts usually begins when the object is buried before it has a chance to become extensively decayed. The organism sinks into a bog or a marsh, or to the bottom of a lake, sea, or river. In some rare cases, it is buried by wind-driven sands. Even after burial, decay can occur and decompose the soft body parts, which emphasizes again that the hard parts are the ones that most commonly survive as fossils. The buried parts that do not decay are preserved, and as the mud or sand hardens to rock, the fossil becomes entombed.

Fossilization is thus a hit-or-miss affair. Only those organisms become fossilized that happen to die in a spot where they can be buried by natural processes before their carcasses are destroyed by scavengers. Also, we should not expect many fossils of forms that live, for example, along a rocky tidal coast, for the pounding waves would demolish many forms and the unstable sediments would not preserve those that escaped the wave action. Similarly, animals living in mountainous areas have little chance of fossilization, because animal remains have small chance of preservation in fast-moving mountain streams. The most likely places for the formation of fossils are in the muddy or sandy bottoms of lakes and oceans, in rivers with quietly moving waters, and in flood plains. We must conclude, then, that only a tiny fraction of animals escape decay or dismemberment by scavengers or other destruction and become fossils. Thus fossils are a minute and selected sample of the animals of the past.

Most fossils are uncovered by erosion. Fossil-bearing rocks become exposed by the actions of wind, rain, and rivers. The work of the paleontologist (one who studies fossils) then begins. The relatively well-preserved specimens that are not too damaged by erosion are removed by very careful excavations. Extraneous material is painstakingly chipped and flaked away in order to minimize damage to the specimen. If the specimen is a skeleton, the position of each bone is precisely recorded as it is removed. The specimens themselves are often specially treated to preserve their shape and structure. The pieces are then packed and shipped to a museum or laboratory for future study. In spite of the arduous, but often exciting, work of paleontologists, only a very small portion of the animals which have been fossilized are recovered, for most of the fossils remain embedded in rock or are destroyed by geological changes or by the elements, if they should be exposed to the atmosphere. Of the tiny fraction of animals that become fossilized, therefore, only a small portion ever reach our attention.

Once the fossils are unearthed, paleontologists try to determine their age or their position in the historical sequence of life. The *absolute* age of

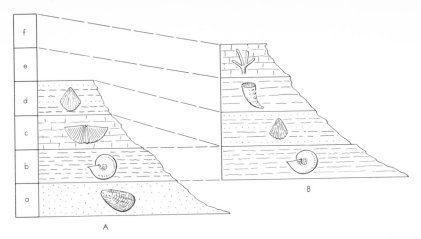

Fig. 16. Correlation and sequence in fossils. A and B are strata of fossil-bearing rock from two different localities. The correlation of the strata is indicated diagrammatically by the oversize fossils. Actually, the strata would be characterized by the whole fossil fauna, not by just one type of fossil. The faunal sequence, a-f, is shown at the left; one discontinuity in the sequence is present in B.

a fossil is difficult to calculate and the older the fossil the less precise the calculation. The technical problems involved here are important and fascinating but must be omitted for lack of space.

The determination of the *relative* age of a fossil rests on the following very simple principle. If objects are layered one on top of the other, the ones on the bottom must have been there first. In the case of paleontology, those fossils that appear in the lower strata of rocks must be the older ones, since the sediments containing the lower group of fossils had to be in place before the other sediments could accumulate on top of them. In any continuous vertical accumulation of fossil-bearing rock, then, the oldest fossils are on the bottom, the newest on top.

If we make the reasonable assumption that similar animals lived at the same time in the past, we can use this fact to relate fossil forms from widely separated sites. For example, the fossil remains of a small herbivore designated as *Hyracotherium* are found in the colored clays and sandstones of New Mexico, and also in the geological deposits in England known as London Clay. These strata in England and in the United States, therefore, are thought to belong to the same geological age. It should also follow that the sequences of fossils above and below the New Mexico *Hyracotherium* would be found above and below the *Hyracotherium* of England, and vice versa. But this may not be the case, for certain sediments might appear in one area and not in the other; erosion, for example, could have worn away a particular stratum in New Mexico but not in England. Although the sequence of forms may be *a, b, c, d* in England, going from older to younger fossil forms, in New Mexico it may be *a, b, d*. The *sequence* of forms in the two areas is not really changed; it is only that a stratum present in one area may be absent in the other (Fig. 16).

39

When we discover fossils, remove and study them as remains of past life, determine their age and their place in the historical sequence of life, and correlate fauna from different parts of the world, we compile what we call the *fossil record*.

The Fossil Record

MAJOR FEATURES

Although many hundreds of thousands of fossils have been studied, they include only a minute fraction of the total number of animals that have lived on the earth. Because it is such a small fraction, and thus incomplete, some may argue that there is little significance in our discoveries to date. Others may take the opposite tack and, by emphasizing the large number of fossils examined disregard the obvious sources of misinterpretation that may arise from small, selected samples. A third position is also possible. We can be aware of the inadequacies in the

PART I TIME SPANS (Rough estimates of years × 10⁶)				PART II			P
Years ago	DURATION Eras	Periods	Epochs	Eras	Geologic periods Periods	Epochs	Biological history: the relative nu
0.025		1.5	0.025		Quaternary	Recent	
1.5			1.475			Pleistocene	
12	70	68.5	10.5	Cenozoic	Tertiary	Pliocene	
25			13			Miocene	
34			9			Oligocene	
60			26			Eocene	
70			10			Paleocene	
132	155	62		Mesozoic	Cretaceous		
180		48			Jurassic		
225		45			Triassic		
275	375	50		Paleozoic	Permian	(Epoch divisions not necessary for present purposes)	
310		35			Pennsylvanian		
350		40			Mississippian		
405		55			Devonian		
430		25			Silurian		
485		55			Ordovician		
600		115			Cambrian		
4500?		3900?		Pre-Cambrian	(Period divisions not well established)		

fossil record, make the appropriate allowance for them, and, at the same time, constructively use what appears to be reliable. This third position seems the most sensible and will be the one we will adopt in this book.

Certain of the broad features of the animal fossil record can best be seen in tabular form (see Fig. 17). Let us start with Part I of the figure, which deals with time spans. Note that the present time appears at the top of the table and the ages grow older as we progress down the table. Since the time periods are so enormous, they are most conveniently expressed in terms of millions of years; thus 600 means 600,000,000 years (or 600×10^6). The left-hand column of figures represents our estimate of how long ago a certain geological age commenced. The figure 600 in this column means we estimate that the Paleozoic era began about six hundred million years ago. The right-hand column gives the estimated duration of each of the periods.

In Part II are the names given to the various time spans of the

Fig. 17. The broad features of the fossil record.

representatives of each group	PART IV
	Geological event
	Glacial conditions, followed by recent times.
	Warm climates, gradually cooling; continental areas mainly free of seas; continued growth of mountains, including Alps and Himalayas.
Arthropoda · Chordata	At first great swamp deposits, followed by birth of Rocky Mountains and Andes, and cooling of climates.
	Much of continental lowlands are near sea-level.
	Widespread desert conditions.
	Continued mountain-building, and variable climates including aridity and perhaps glaciation.
	Lands low and warm with seas over much of continents, at the beginning; coal swamps, from which come the greatest of our coal deposits; mountain-building toward the end.
	Still considerable portions of land below water; evidences of aridity and continental areas.
	Much of land below the sea at first, followed by mountain-building at the end.
	Great submergence of lands.
	Lowlands and mild climates; first abundantly fossiliferous rocks.
? — Worm-like phyla especially Annelida	

history of the earth. The largest time periods are called *eras* (we have already mentioned the Paleozoic era). Each era is broken up into *periods,* the oldest one of the Paleozoic being the Cambrian, and within the periods are *epochs,* which are most important in discussing the Cenozoic era. Occasionally two eras, the Proterozoic and Archaeozoic, are listed before the Paleozoic and would appear, therefore, sometime between the formation of the earth, which occurred roughly—very roughly—four and a half billion years ago, and the beginning of the Paleozoic. There is little advantage in us breaking down this Pre-Cambrian span into even such large time spans as eras, since we know too little about this period to attempt to define any meaningful time span within it. Here we shall refer to it simply as the Pre-Cambrian. The eras, periods, and epochs in the upper part of the table will concern us most, and the reader must learn their names, especially the names of the various eras, and know the approximate duration of each.

Part III represents diagrammatically the relative number of organisms in the major phyla as measured by their *known* number of fossil *genera.* Remember that the time sequence shown in Parts I and II also applies here. For instance, very few fossil genera of the Protozoa have been found from the early, or lower, Paleozoic, but in the later, or upper, Paleozoic they show up in large numbers, and in the Cenozoic their fossils are very common. Similarly, one can follow the fate of other phyla through half a billion years in terms of the abundance of their known fossil genera. One of the striking features of this record is the relative lack of fossils from the Pre-Cambrian. A few are known, and among these many are clearly algae, a relatively simple plant. Some authorities claim to have found the shells of certain protozoans in Pre-Cambrian deposits, but others doubt the validity of such discoveries. If this difference of opinion is resolved in favor of those claiming to have found Pre-Cambrian remains of protozoans, such fossils would represent the oldest evidence we have of animal life. Members of all the major fossil-producing phyla except the Chordata are represented in the Cambrian, and these fossils reveal that Cambrian animals were quite complex organisms, not as complex perhaps as those found later in these groups, but still highly differentiated organisms in terms of what we might expect for each phylum (Fig. 18). The chordates first appear in the Silurian as jawless, armor-plated fishes called ostracoderms (shell-skinned).

By the early Paleozoic, then, some 400 million years ago, all the major fossil-producing phyla were in existence. Since certain phyla that contain members with predominantly soft bodies, e.g., the Annelida and Platyhelminthes, have left occasional fossils, such as tracks in the mud, it is reasonable to assume they were also present at the beginning of the Paleozoic, and perhaps even in large numbers. One other point to note in Part III is the change in the abundance of fossils. For example, bryozoan fossils are plentiful in the Ordovician and Silurian and then

Fig. 18. Reconstruction of a Cambrian sea showing seaweed, sponges, sea cucumbers, worms, brachiopods, trilobites, and crustaceans. (Photo courtesy Chicago Museum of Natural History.)

gradually decrease in number, only to reappear strongly in the late Mesozoic. Note also that the phylum Graptolithina is known only from the fossil record; these animals lived apparently just during the Paleozoic.

Since in the Tertiary most phyla show more fossil genera than in the Cambrian, we might conclude that there was a diversification of life from the Cambrian to the Cenozoic Tertiary. Although this is a possible interpretation, we could also conclude that we have more fossils from 75 million years ago than from 500 million years, because the younger fossils lie in the upper, more readily examined strata. These younger fossil-bearing rocks have also had less time to undergo geological metamorphoses that could obliterate fossils if they were present. The only way to decide this question is to look at the fossils within any given phylum and see if there is any direct evidence for diversity. We will do this after we briefly examine the last part of the figure, Part IV.

The important point to remember from Part IV is that the physical nature of the surface of the earth has been continually changing and still is doing so. Shallow seas once stood where continental land masses jut up today, and mountains have pushed up where before there were none. The position of the north and south poles has varied and so has the general climate of the earth through the many millions of years. It is hard to realize that the Sahara desert was once a fertile, productive land and that palm trees once grew in Greenland, but such are the conclusions we must draw from the fossil record. These drastic changes undoubtedly affected the organisms living at that time. The transition from the Paleozoic to the Mesozoic was a period of great geological turmoil that left its mark on almost all animal groups. In this Permian-Triassic period, almost all groups show evidence of a decrease in number.

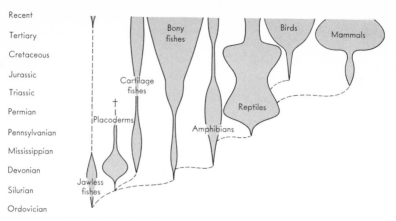

Fig. 19. The broad outlines of vertebrate fossil history.

Not only did the numbers of fossils from different geological eras and periods vary, so did the kinds of fossils. Any major taxon we study would show this. Let us look at the vertebrates, a subphylum of the Chordata, and one of the more clearly documented examples. Figure 19 shows a number of the various known fossil genera of Vertebrata. This diagram is a breakdown of the chordate column in Part III of Fig. 17. In it we see that the ostracoderms (jawless fishes) died out by the end of the Devonian and that another group of primitive fishes, the placoderms, were abundant then but died out, too, by the end of the Paleozoic.

Fishes with cartilaginous skeletons, such as the sharks today possess, first appeared in the Devonian, followed by bony fishes with skeletons similar to those in today's trout and mackerel. These two groups of fishes have persisted to the present, with the bony fishes being very numerous. Amphibians, the group that includes our present-day frogs, toads, newts, and salamanders, next appeared, in the Devonian, marking the first real invasion of land by vertebrates. (Invertebrate arthropods and plants were already on land.) The reptiles appeared in large numbers toward the close of the Paleozoic, were pinched a bit by the Permian-Triassic geologic crisis, but came back to dominate the Mesozoic, which was the Age of Reptiles, the period of the great dinosaurs (Fig. 20). Birds and mammals appeared separately in the late and early Mesozoic, respectively, and greatly increased their numbers in the Cenozoic.

Within each of the vertebrate classes, new forms were appearing, and disappearing, in the fossil record. Figure 21 shows the rate of appearance of new genera during the various geological periods. One paleontologist has ventured that not more than one per cent of the four-limbed vertebrates (amphibians, reptiles, birds, and mammals) living in early mid-Mesozoic times have living descendants today. Perhaps the most spectacular decline was the extinction of those magnificent reptiles, the dinosaurs. There has been, then, an enormous turnover in the kinds of animals that have lived on the earth.

We should note here that some vertebrates have been similar in

Fig. 20. Painting of a Mesozoic landscape showing a carnivorous reptile (center, *Tyrannosaurus*) and other herbivorous ones. Also represented is a flying reptile. (Photo courtesy Peabody Museum of Natural History, Yale University.)

Fig. 21. Rate of appearance of new vertebrate fossil genera from the Ordovician to the Tertiary periods. The sketches represent, from left to right, jawless fishes, placoderms, reptiles, amphibians, fishes, and mammals; the pointers indicate the period of greatest abundance (redrawn from Simpson).

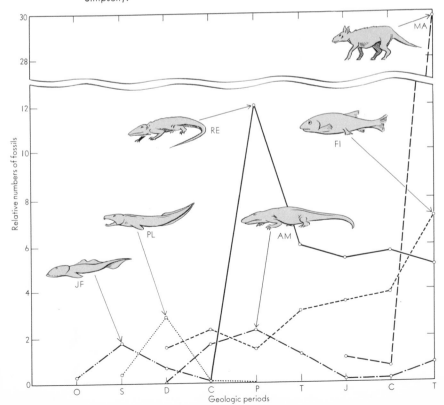

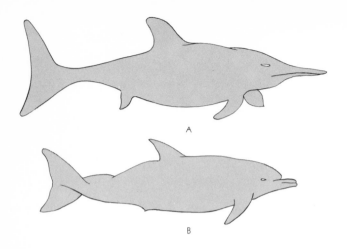

Fig. 22. Similarities in external form of certain aquatic vertebrates. (A) Ichthyosaur; (B) dolphin.

form to other groups of animals. For instance, the now extinct ichthyosaur, from what we have been able to reconstruct of its appearance from fossils, probably looked very much like our present-day dolphins (Fig. 22). The ichthyosaur was an aquatic reptile and the dolphin is a mammal. Both are vertebrates, it is true, but they are members of two distinctly different classes and yet show quite a striking degree of similarity in external characters. Other animals have also been known to have such similarity in external form.

This picture of the vertebrate fossil history could be repeated for other groups. In the Arthropoda, the trilobites (Fig. 23), once a very common early Paleozoic form, eventually disappeared, and the eurypterids, or so-called water scorpions (Fig. 24), shared the same fate. During the mid-Paleozoic, the arthropods evolved the new forms of the land-invaders. In the Mollusca, snail-like and clam-like forms are common in the late Ordovician, as are the nautiloid cephalopods (Fig. 23).

Fig. 23. Reconstruction of an Ordovician sea with seaweed, coral, brachiopods, clams, snails, cephalopods, and trilobites. (Photo courtesy Chicago Museum of Natural History.)

Fig. 24. Reconstruction of a Silurian sea, emphasizing eurypterids with associated snails, crustaceans, worms, and seaweed. (Photo courtesy Chicago Museum of Natural History.)

Another important mollusc group, the ammonites, appear in the Silurian (Fig. 24). Today we have the modern snails, clams, and the chambered *Nautilus*, but the ammonites disappeared by the end of the Mesozoic. In each group, new forms appear and old ones die out. Only rarely do forms seem to persist unchanged for long periods of time.

Now let us summarize the major features that have emerged from our description of the fossil record. (1) The fossil record covers a time span of at least half a billion years. Prior to that time, in the Pre-Cambrian, only a few fossils of relatively simple plants are definitely known. A significant fossil record exists only for the time from the Cambrian down to the present day, and this time span is divided into various eras, periods, and epochs.

(2) The Cambrian fossils represent all the major phyla that produce fossils except the phylum Chordata. The chordates appear in the fossil record in the early Silurian. The first land animals, which were invertebrates, appear in this period, too. Land vertebrates first appear later, in the Devonian. About 200,000,000 years ago, at the end of the Paleozoic or the beginning of the Mesozoic, a crisis occurred in living forms, as is evidenced by an almost universal decrease in the number of fossil genera. This disaster probably resulted from extensive changes in the earth's surface. Following this crisis, certain new forms became common, of which the most striking are the reptiles. During the last 70,000,000 years—in the Cenozoic, that is—birds and mammals have come to occupy an important number of the earth's habitats.

(3) In the past three eras of the world's history, the fossil record reveals that there has been a general increase in the total number of genera in the different phyla. This means, of course, that new genera have arisen during these times, although we also know that old ones have disappeared. Most terrestrial forms apparently die out over the course of several hundred million years; very few survive. In some cases, forms from distinctly different groups come to resemble each other, but mostly there appears an increase in diversity.

Before leaving the fossil record, we should take a close look at a selected portion of it. By examining a form that has a fairly complete fossil history, we can gain a detailed insight into the fossil record. In the previous section, we discussed this record largely in terms of phyla and classes; in this section, we will look at what goes on within a family, and none is more informative than the family, Equidae, which contains, among other forms, the modern horse, *Equus*.

We will begin the history of the horse family (Fig. 25) with *Hyracotherium*, more commonly called eohippus, the "dawn horse." This animal lived in the early Eocene epoch of the Cenozoic, about 60,000,000 years ago. It was tiny compared to modern horses, being about the size of a wire-haired terrier. Its relatively small teeth appear to be those of a browser, i.e., an animal that feeds on leaves and twigs, and the teeth have low crowns—that is, the chewing or grinding surfaces are not especially thick. The patterns or conformations of the crowns, in terms of the bumps or cusps and of the ridges between them, were not very complex, and the molar teeth were clearly different from the premolars. In the skull, the distance from the nose to the eye, which contains the tooth-bearing part of the skull, is about equal to the distance from the eye to the base of the skull. Another important feature is the limbs, especially the feet. The forefeet of eohippus show four toes and a fifth bone splint; the hindfeet show three toes and two bone splints, which are clearly interpretable as the first and fifth toes, apparently no longer used by eohippus but still present in this somewhat reduced form.

As we pass from strata containing the oldest remains of *Hyracotherium* or eohippus to younger Eocene strata, we find fossils that remind us of eohippus but that are distinctly different. By the middle and late Eocene, these differences are so pronounced that we recognize a new form called *Orohippus*, and eohippus as we first knew it is no longer present. *Orohippus* is larger than eohippus and, unlike the case in eohippus, its last premolar looks very much like a molar. As we continue in time, through the Oligocene to the lower Miocene, we find that the definitive *Orohippus* remains disappear and forms differing from it sufficiently to be called a new name, *Mesohippus*, appear. It is quite impossible to say just when the typical *Mesohippus* took the place of *Orohippus*, for the successive differences in the skeletal remains are so slight only a very continuous gradation of forms separates the two. The same gradual stages exist also between *Hyracotherium* and *Orohippus*.

The typical *Mesohippus* is larger than *Orohippus*; it has only three functional toes on its front feet and three of its premolars are clearly molar-like. These teeth are bigger than the premolars of eohippus, and the jaws have lengthened to accommodate these teeth, making the nose to eye length longer than the eye to skull-base length. But from the shape of the cusps and ridges and from the height of the tooth crown, which is still relatively low, we conclude these animals continued to be browsers.

After another continuous gradation of slight differences, we find a further distinct form emerging in the Miocene, i.e., *Merychippus*. The body size is larger than in any of the foregoing forms. Each foot still has three toes, but the two outermost ones probably do not touch the ground. In effect, then, *Merychippus* stands on only a single toe on each foot. The teeth have changed markedly. Not only do they show high crowns, but they have a kind of cement-filling in between the cusps and ridges; and the pattern of the cusps and ridges has become more complex. Since these teeth are clearly better suited to grinding than are those of *Mesohippus*, *Orohippus,* or eohippus, we can infer that *Merychippus* is no longer a browser but a grazer that feeds on tough grasses which would wear the teeth down to useless stubs if they did not have some extra protection. The high crowns, cement, and complex surface are exactly what a grass grazer needs to grind up its food. It is very hard now to distinguish premolars from molars.

Pliohippus is the new larger form that appears in the Pliocene, separated from *Merychippus* by, once again, a series of slightly different forms. In *Pliohippus*, the feet are definitely one-toed, for only splints remain of the other toes. The jaw is much elongated to hold the large, high-crowned grinding teeth. *Equus*, the modern horse, which first appeared in the Pleistocene, after another series of graduated differences, shows the special features of *Pliohippus* to an even more extreme degree.

Although we represent our sequence of fossil development with a series of six distinct forms, *the actual fossil record shows no such discontinuities.* In addition, the forms we use to show this chain of evolution had many side branches. Figure 26 shows the various other fossil forms we know today. From this it is clear that some seventeen different fossil genera of horses can be distinguished, and all are joined, through a series of slight differences, to *Hyracotherium*, the little eohippus of the Eocene.

What can we conclude from this description of the fossil Equidae? First, this extensive collection of fossils presents a very continuous array of slight differences. Second, these continuities are so clear that we can construct a chain of slightly different fossils connecting the dog-sized, many-toed browser of fifty million years ago with the large, single-toed grazing horses of today. Finally, although we have no space here to document other cases, we are justified in saying that whenever man has been able to study in detail the fossil history of a given group of animals, he has found the same pattern of many, slight, successive differences.

We now end our description of the fossil record and turn to the problems that led us to study it. These are the predictions concerning temporal diversity.

FIRST PREDICTION: CHANGE IN TIME

It is clear that, *in itself,* the presence of successively different forms through a period of time is not evidence of change in those forms. We

		Formations in Western United States: the characteristic types of horses in each
Quatenary or Age of Man	Recent	
	Pleistocene	Equus
Tertiary or Age of Mammals	Pliocene	Pliohippus
	Miocene	Merychippus
	Oligocene	Mesohippus
	Eocene	Orohippus
	Paleocene	Eohippus
Age of Reptiles	Cretaceous Jurassic Triassic	

Forefoot	Hind foot	Teeth	
One toe Splints of 2nd and 4th digits	One toe Splints of 2nd and 4th digits	Long- crowned. cement- covered	
Three toes Side toes not touching the ground	Three toes Side toes not touching the ground		
Three toes Side toes touching the ground. Splint of 5th digit	Three toes Side toes touching the ground	Short- crowned, without cement	
Four toes	Three toes Splints of 1st and 5th digit		
Hypothetical ancestors with five toes on each foot and teeth like those of monkeys, etc.		The premolar teeth become more and more like true molars.	

Fig. 25. Fossil history of the horse from *Eohippus* to *Equus* (after Dodson).

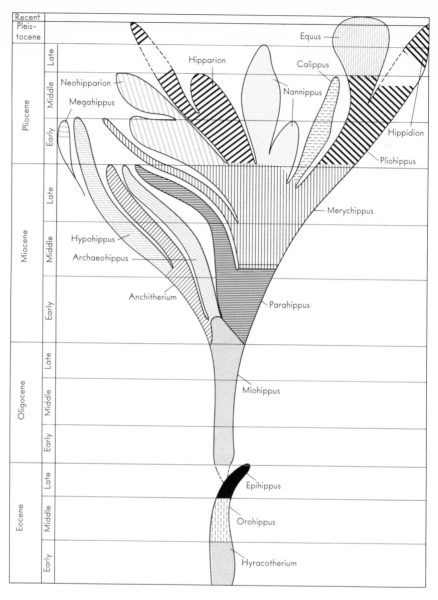

Fig. 26. Fossil history of the *Equidae* (after Mayr, Linsley, and Usinger).

could explain different forms, as did Linnaeus and the young Darwin, by assuming they were specially created at different periods in time, and that one form did not and could not change into another. But if we use evolution as an explanatory hypothesis, we should expect two things: (1) to be able to arrange the fossils in a graded sequence in terms of their differences in form, with the most different forms lying at opposite ends of the sequence; and (2) to find the most similar fossils closest together in the fossil-bearing strata. As we have seen, this is precisely what we do find in the parts of the fossil record that have been carefully studied—in the history of the Equidae and also in the history of the invertebrates. Furthermore, we can also say something about the nature of these changes. The size of the individual changes seems on the whole to be small, on the order of what we would expect from hereditary mutations. The fossil record of the horse again supports this viewpoint. Therefore, since the data from the fossil record coincide so closely with what we would predict if evolutionary change had actually occurred, we can conclude that fossils provide evidence of evolutionary change in time.

Some paleontologists and geneticists, however, believe that mutations of profound effect, i.e., those that greatly change the appearance or phenotype of the animal, are also significant in the history of animal life. Most students of evolution discount this theory on the basis that such large changes would not enable the animal to adapt sufficiently in order to survive, since a delicately organized system can be transformed only so much and still function efficiently. But strong arguments have been made for these so-called macromutations, and they are known to occur. Whether or not they are of evolutionary significance is still being debated. If they are, we might expect evidence of them in the fossil record, in the form of large differences between neighboring stages in a fossil sequence. Such gaps are claimed, for example, in the fossil record of certain invertebrates, but these gaps can also be explained by the disappearance of certain strata containing fossils from the few million years in question. Gaps in the record, then, may have resulted from the fact that a mutational change has had profound phenotypic effects, or, as is more likely, from the fact that part of the record has been destroyed by climatic or geological catastrophes.

SECOND PREDICTION: ORIENTED CHANGE

Our second prediction was that we should find evidence of a direction in the evolutionary changes of the fossil record, from less complex to more complex forms. We must admit that good evidence of such an orientation is lacking. The area where fossil evidence would be most informative—that recording the rise of the major phyla of the cellular animals from the simpler acellular state—is entirely absent from the fossil record. Presumably all this evolution was in the Pre-Cambrian. We are left, then, with only Cambrian and post-Cambrian data.

Some modern forms are definitely more complex than earlier forms. The vertebrates today, for instance, are obviously more complicated organisms than the primitive Paleozoic fishes, the ostracoderms or placoderms. (Such comparisons really depend on a detailed anatomical study, for which we have no space here.) We could also argue that most contemporary forms have evolved more complex sensory systems than existed back in the Paleozoic, which is perhaps only another way of saying that selection pressures extending over 500 million years have probably wrought certain changes in the direction of better adaptation, resulting in more complex organisms. But this is not an altogether convincing argument, because we have no way of knowing how well a fossil animal was adapted to its environment. In certain fossil forms, such as the ammonites, we have definite evidence that the coilings and markings on their shells slowly increased and then decreased in complexity.

To sum up, although animal forms seem to have increased in complexity, we do not have enough evidence to prove this as a general phenomenon. One reason is our lack of fossils that record the early history of animal evolution. Another is the lack of consistency in the evidence we do have; some evidence favors the prediction and some does not, e.g., the ammonites. A large part of the fossil record does not say much either way, since it only tells us that well-differentiated and highly evolved forms were present in the Paleozoic and are also present today in those same groups.

THIRD PREDICTION: EXTINCTION, EMERGENCE, DIVERGENCE, AND CONVERGENCE

The answer to this prediction should already be obvious. The fossil record supplies convincing evidence that certain forms die out (dinosaurs), that new forms emerge (terrestrial animals), that forms diverge (some vertebrates diverge into land dwellers and fliers, others remain aquatic), and that certain forms even converge (ichthyosaurs and dolphins).

Indeed, it is really impossible to look at the fossil record and not see the great flux and transformation that everywhere characterizes it. Change is a dominant feature of that record, just as it is of evolution as a whole. We have proposed that the underlying cause of this change is the ever constant pressure on organisms to become better adapted in the face of a changing environment. In principle this idea is fine, but in practice it is difficult to demonstrate from the fossil record. We are not at all clear why the dinosaurs became extinct; they were grand creatures who exploited aquatic and terrestrial habitats, and also evolved flying forms. They probably died out for some reason related to natural selection, but we cannot say just what the reason was.

New forms can emerge slowly or rapidly. Extremely slow change is seen in such forms as the oppossum or certain oysters, where contemporary forms are little changed from those living many millions of years ago. Rapid change is exemplified by the horses. Note in Fig. 26 what a diversification appears in the grazer, *Merychippus*. Such a diverging burst is called an *adaptive radiation*. In the case of *Merychippus*, it was probably caused by the opening up of a new habitat, the grasslands, which the grazing horses, along with other herbivores, were able to exploit.

A phenomenon that is similar to convergence, but different from it, is that of *parallelism*. Convergence, as we have seen, is the adaptation to a common mode of life. Take the reptilian ichthyosaur and mammalian dolphin: to survive, both had to become predatory marine animals de-

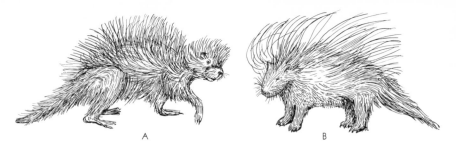

Fig. 27. Parallelism in porcupines. (A) South American porcupine; (B) African porcupine.

pendent on fast swimming. The fact that such similar appearances could evolve out of such different ancestry indicates both the plasticity of living form and the powerful forces of selective pressures. Parallelism, on the other hand, is the independent evolution by two or more closely related forms of common features not present in the common ancestral form.

An excellent example is found in the evolution of the South American and African porcupines (Fig. 27). The fossil evidence indicates that the common ancestor of these two species was not a porcupine but a now extinct rodent that had a world-wide distribution. In South America and in Africa, the descendants of this non-porcupine rodent exploited certain niches and evolved independently into perfectly good porcupines.

Conclusions

Our first prediction—that animals change in time through the accumulation of many small changes—is realized. The succession of forms found in the fossil record is in complete accord with our evolutionary hypothesis. The third prediction—that certain animal forms become extinct, new ones emerge, and others diverge and converge—is also realized. The reason for extinction is not always known, but its occurrence is an observable fact. It is clear that new forms result from the continuous change of a given line or by the divergence of a line into adaptive radiations. Convergence of distantly related animal forms and parallel changes in more closely related forms are also known.

The second prediction—that change takes place from less to more complex forms—is not realized. The problem here is twofold: (1) the evidence we have is equivocal regarding increasing complexity—the chordates, for instance, show it, but the ammonites do not, and (2) the lack of Pre-Cambrian fossils precludes a study of the early evolution of the invertebrate phyla, an area of critical importance for this prediction. We can come to no distinct conclusions regarding this prediction and so will set it aside for the present. On the basis of the first and third predictions, however, we can conclude that evolution is an acceptable explanation of animal diversity.

In the previous chapter, we tested predictions regarding temporal diversity, and in this one we will test the following predictions which concern spatial diversity: (1) different forms of animals represent different modes of life; (2) certain geographical regions, such as continents, will possess a characteristic fauna; and (3) a given mode of life can be exploited by animals from different taxa.

As in the discussion of temporal diversity, we must first acquaint ourselves with certain data and concepts before we can make meaningful analyses of our predictions. The area of biology that now concerns us is *ecology*, which is the study of the interaction of organisms or groups of organisms with their environment, and we will begin our investigation with a discussion of *habitats* and *niches*.

Habitats and Niches

The habitat of an organism has been compared to a man's address, and its niche to the man's profession. The habitat defines where an organism lives; its niche describes its mode of life in that habitat. A habitat obviously can contain more than one niche. For example, the zebra and the African lion both roam the veldt or tropical grassland, but they do not have the same niche. The zebra is a herbivore that lives off the veldt vegetation, while the lion is a carnivore that feeds on veldt herbivores, including the zebra itself. Or take another example: Both the oceanic tuna and the herring

7

Spatial Diversity: Ecological Zoogeography

occupy the same habitat (i.e., the surface waters of the ocean) and both are carnivores—the tuna feeds on the herring and the herring on tiny animal forms known as zooplankton. But they occupy different niches, largely because they pursue different food organisms.

In relating an organism, or a population of a certain kind of organism, to its environment, defining its habitat is just the beginning, for accurate knowledge of its niche is our real goal. To describe the ecological niches of organisms, we must understand the functioning of natural populations, and to do this we must consider a great many factors: the number of organisms in the population, the sources of their food, how rapidly or efficiently they metabolize as a group, the effect of the nonliving or abiotic environment (i.e., temperature, humidity, oxygen availability, etc.), the effect of the organisms on the abiotic environment, the interactions that occur within the group or between this group and other ones, and so forth—in other words, all the multifarious activities of organisms that in some way, directly or indirectly, determine their mode of life.

Some niches are more complicated than others. For instance, the niches at the bottom of oceanic trenches or in certain caves are relatively less complex than those in a forest or shallow lake, for in the former many of the conditions bearing on the niche—temperature, light, amount of moisture—are far more constant than in the latter. Differences in the complexity of niches also depend on the organisms themselves. Those organisms with complex life cycles usually occupy more than one niche. The mosquito larva, for example, feeds on microscopic aquatic forms found in shallow water, but as an adult it is airborne and feeds on vertebrate blood—a quite different mode of life.

The animal that causes malaria in man, to take a second example, lives in two hosts, the *Anopheles* mosquito and man. In man this parasite has three different phases in its life cycle, and each is passed in a different part of the human body. The first phase occurs in certain cells of tissues such as the liver; the second one occurs in the red blood cells; and the third is in the blood fluid outside the red blood cells. In the mosquito, this parasite passes again through different stages, one in the gut, a second in the gut wall, and a third in the salivary glands (Fig. 2c). Since the malarial organism looks quite different in each of these six different phases, it probably means that it carries on different functions in each, and thus has a different niche for each stage of its life cycle. Although this is pushing the concept of the niche to an extreme, it does illustrate that a niche is the composite of many factors, which differ in the various stages of a single organism, as well as between entirely different organisms.

Ecosystems

No organism lives in a vacuum, for organisms and their environment are inseparably interrelated and interactive. A system of interacting live organisms and nonliving substances forms what we call an *ecosystem,* which can be conveniently broken up into four components: (1) abiotic substances, (2) producers, (3) consumers, and (4) decomposers.

The *abiotic substances* of an ecosystem are the nonliving parts and consist of inorganic materials such as water, carbon dioxide, oxygen, calcium, nitrogen, phosphorus, phosphorus compounds, and so on. They also include some organic matter, such as amino acids and other products of the decay of living things.

The *producers* are those living members of the ecosystem that are capable of making food from inorganic compounds and, if necessary, from organic compounds. Usually, sunlight is also needed since the producers are largely photosynthetic plants. In a dense forest, the trees are the most important producers; in a grassland, the grasses are; in lakes, the producers are rooted or floating water plants and microscopic plants, usually algae; in the ocean, the algae—some rooted along coasts, others floating in the open sea—are the producers.

The *consumers* are those organisms that ingest other organisms. As used here, *ingestion* refers to the intake of food matter, such as bacteria by the amoeba, worms by the robin, or flesh by the lion. The food is then digested, that is, broken down to molecular dimensions, within the ingestor's body. The vast majority of consumers are animals, and the primary consumers in any particular habitat are herbivores, which feed on the producers. A deer is a primary consumer in a forest and a bison is one on a prairie. Microscopic animals, such as Protozoa and certain Crustacea, which feed on the floating algae of ponds or seas, are primary consumers in their habitats. Secondary consumers, the carnivores that feed on the primary consumers, are quite common, and the food chain often extends to secondary carnivores, those animals that eat the carnivores which consume the herbivorous consumers.

The *decomposers* are chiefly microorganisms such as fungi and bacteria whose role in the ecosystem is to assimilate the protoplasm of other organisms. Assimilation is clearly differentiated from ingestion in that *assimilation* is a two-stage process: First, the assimilating organism releases materials into the environment that reduce the protoplasm of other organisms to roughly molecular dimensions; in the second step, this molecular food is absorbed into the assimilator's body to be further digested if necessary. The decomposers of an ecosystem usually concentrate on the protoplasm of dead producers and consumers. They then discharge the end products of their physiological activity into the environment as relatively simple organic, or in a few cases inorganic, compounds, which in turn are utilizable by the producers. The molds, mushrooms, and toadstools of the forest floor are the largest members of the decomposers and are visible to the naked eye; the bacteria are too small to be seen without special equipment unless they accumulate as colonies.

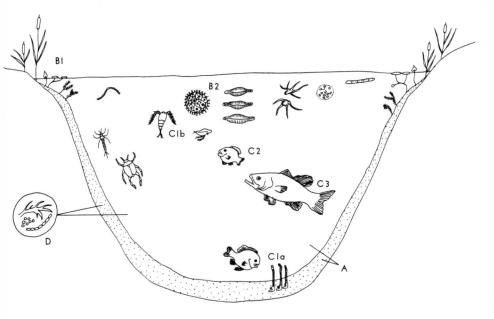

Fig. 28. Diagram of a pond ecosystem. (A) Abiotic substances composed of inorganic and organic material, including water and the products of decomposed protoplasm. (B1) Producers, the rooted plants. (B2) Producers, the phytoplankton or microscopic, nonrooted plants. (C1a) Primary consumers, the bottom-dwelling herbivores, including certain worms and crustaceans. (C1b) Primary consumers, the herbivorous zooplankton (microscopic animals) which feed on the phytoplankton. (C2) Secondary consumers or primary carnivores, feeding on the primary consumers. (C3) Tertiary consumers or secondary carnivores, feeding on the primary carnivores. (D) Decomposers, certain bacteria and fungi which break down protoplasm to the level of abiotic substances. (Redrawn from Odum.)

In an ecosystem, then, the last three of the four components are composed of living things. Plants are the predominant producers, animals the consumers, and certain microorganisms the decomposers. In Fig. 28, the fresh-water pond is presented as an example of an ecosystem. Some ecosystems lack one or another of the components. In the depths of the ocean, for example, there are no producers, but their place is taken by the shower of dead and decaying protoplasm that sinks from the surface. Other aquatic communities are sometimes devoid of consumers for short periods, and decomposers will attack the producers directly, although usually only when the plants are dead. Microbial, plant, and animal organisms all have their special niches in an ecosystem, which is the fundamental unit in ecology. With these basic terms and concepts in mind, we will discuss first the interactions of certain populations in nature and then describe animal habitats systematically.

Population Interactions

Within the complexity of an ecosystem, organisms achieve a high degree of specialization in pursuing their various modes of life. In the preceding section, mention was made of the relationships of producers, consumers, and decomposers. In this section, our attention centers on the consumers, the animal component of the ecosystem, for in studying the interaction of animal populations, especially population competition, we gain some insight into the delicate adjustments present in the exploitation of animal niches.

Population interactions can generally be classified as positive, neutral, or negative. In *positive interactions,* at least one of the interacting populations increases in size. *Neutral interaction* is where there is no effect on population size. And *negative interaction* covers those cases where one or both populations decrease in size.

Competition is negative interaction where both populations suffer a decrease in number. The interaction involves competition for food, living space, nesting sites, and so forth, that are needed by both populations, and it ordinarily produces one of two results: One population is removed from the area of conflict—that is, the less successful competitor disappears or is forced to exploit a niche that is not in competition with the dominant form—or an equilibrium is reached allowing both populations to survive, although in a somewhat reduced quantity. Many populations inhabit niches that obviously overlap, and one of the most fascinating problems in ecology is to determine how great the overlap must be before a condition of equilibrium gives way to one of competition. Some light was shed on this question by the contemporary Russian ecologist, Gause, who proposed that only one species occupies a given niche. A niche, you will recall, defines the way organisms live—their profession, if you will—and involves how they get food, how efficiently they utilize it, how they reproduce, how they defend themselves, and so forth. According to the so-called Gause principle, each mode of life is filled by just one species; niches may overlap, but a single niche is inhabited by only one form.

Since this principle bears directly on our conception of competition, let us examine some of the experimental data and field observations that test it. Gause himself performed a classic demonstration of his principle, using two species of the same genus of ciliated Protozoa, *Paramecium aurelia* and *P. caudatum.* By growing the two organisms in similar vessels, containing the same fluid medium and food (a kind of bacterium) and under similar conditions of temperature and light, he made sure that the niches occupied by the two populations were identical. In Fig. 29 we see the results of growing *P. aurelia* and *P. caudatum* by themselves and in the presence of each other. Under the latter conditions, *P. caudatum* was eliminated. In isolation, *P. aurelia* grew more rapidly than *P. caudatum,*

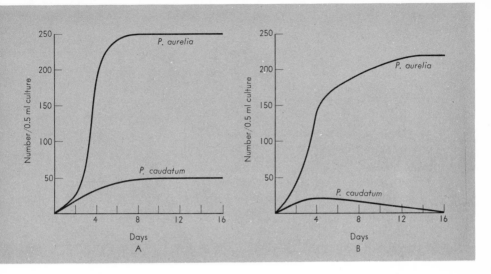

Fig. 29. Growth curves of laboratory cultures of *Paramecium aurelia* and *P. caudatum*. (A) Population densities when the protozoans are grown in separate cultures. (B) Population densities when both species are grown in the same culture.

indicating that *P. aurelia* uses the available food more rapidly and efficiently than does *P. caudatum*. When both occupy the same niche, therefore, we would expect *P. aurelia* to be the more successful competitor.

In another study, two species of flour beetles, *Tribolium castaneum* and *T. confusum*, were also grown separately and as mixed populations. As separate groups, each species established a population of a given density, with *T. confusum* becoming the denser. When the protozoan, *Adelina*, which parasitizes both beetles, was introduced into the isolated cultures, it decreased the *T. castaneum* population by two-thirds but did not affect the *T. confusum* nearly so drastically. The populations of the two beetles were repeatedly mixed, and one or the other invariably became extinct, thus tending to confirm Gause's claim that when two different populations compete for the same niche, one must be displaced. When the parasite was absent, *T. castaneum* usually won out; when *Adelina* was present, *T. confusum* usually dominated, which shows how varying one factor in the niche can determine the final outcome of the competition.

Two more examples, this time from field observations of birds, will further illustrate the Gause principle. The first concerns those charmingly awkward-appearing creatures, flamingos. In Africa the greater flamingo (*Phoenicopterus antiguorum*) feeds in the same shallow lakes where there is also found a very similar-appearing species, the so-called lesser flamingo (*Phoeniconaias minor*). At first glance, we would suspect that such similar birds sharing the same pond must be competing for food, but careful study shows this not to be the case, for fine platelets in the mouth of the lesser flamingo restrict its diet largely to microscopic blue-green algae, while the coarser filter structure in the bill of the greater flamingo allows it to ingest larger food particles, including such small animals as tiny

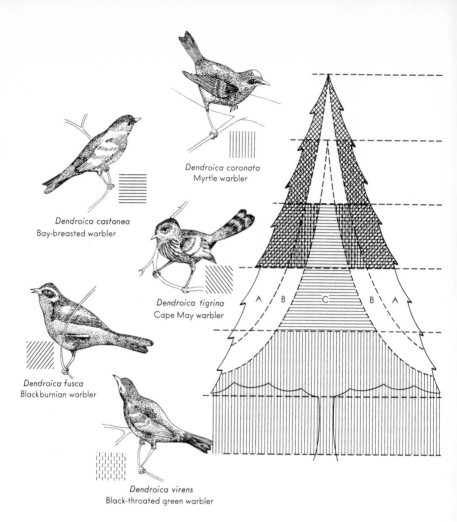

Dendroica coronata
Myrtle warbler

Dendroica castanea
Bay-breasted warbler

Dendroica tigrina
Cape May warbler

Dendroica fusca
Blackburnian warbler

Dendroica virens
Black-throated green warbler

A B C B A

Fig. 30. A diagrammatic representation of the feeding zones in a spruce tree of five species of North American warblers. The tree is divided, vertically, into six zones, each ten feet high. Within the tree, there are three other zones: (A) the outermost zone of new needles and buds, (B) a middle zone of old needles, and (C) the inner zone of bare or lichen-covered branches. The warblers feed in all parts of the tree; the various types of shading indicate the area where each species spends at least half its feeding time.

crustaceans and mud-dwelling insect larvae. Although both species of flamingo eat from the same ponds, they exploit different niches for their food, and thus avoid competition.

Our second example is taken from the food-gathering habits of five species of North American warblers. All five forms can feed in the same spruce tree without competing with one another, because each hunts its insect prey in different parts of the tree (Fig. 30). Each warbler also has its own individual hunting behavior. The Cape May warbler *(Dendroica tigrina)*, for example, moves mostly up and down the tree; the bay-breasted warbler *(D. castanea)* hops around through the branches; and the black-throated green warbler *(D. virens)* closely investigates the dense mats

62

of spruce needles. These warblers, then, roughly partition the tree into different feeding zones, and where the zones overlap competition is minimized by the varying hunting patterns of the birds.

All these examples are in accord with the Gause principle. The laboratory experiments showed that only one species survives when two compete for the same niche. The field studies demonstrated that where certain forms in nature at first seem to occupy the same niche, they actually do not. These and other data confirm Gause's principle so convincingly that we can justifiably conclude there is only one species to a niche.

Animal Habitats

Animals live in all but a few places on the surface of our planet, and our next concern will be to characterize, and to systematize our knowledge of, the various habitats that exist in the oceans, in fresh-water streams and lakes, and on the land masses. We now have the advantage of knowing the rudiments of how populations interact with each other and with the nonliving world. Note that these habitats are more comprehensive in scale than the ecosystems and their constituent niches.

Let us begin with the major marine habitats. These habitats are separated into divisions, the two largest of which are the neritic and the oceanic zones (Fig. 31). The *neritic zone* extends from the high-tide mark to the edge of the continental shelf. The dominant producers in it, and in the deep ocean as well, are floating algae, called *phytoplankton,* although in some locations the algae attached to the bottom also become important

Fig. 31. Oceanic life zones (after Hedgpeth, modified from Odum).

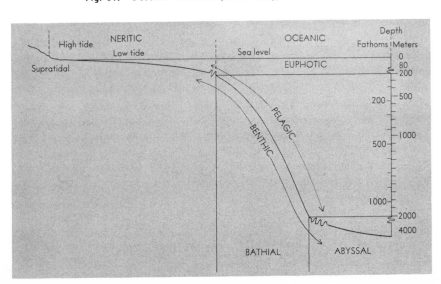

as producers. The animal consumers are of three types: (1) the *zooplank-ton*—small free-swimming or floating forms, (2) the *nekton*—large free-swimming or, more rarely, floating forms, and (3) the *benthos*—bottom-dwelling forms.

Several different phyla are represented in the zooplankton, and the mature forms of protozoans and certain flatworms, segmented worms, molluscs, and arthropods are permanent components of the zooplankton, while other forms are in larval stages and will grow into large organisms that will later become part of either the nekton or the benthos. The nekton are mostly fish, but also include mammals, such as seals and whales, and sea turtles, and certain arthropods and molluscs. Benthic animals come in a great variety of forms and include all the major phyla—we need think only of tide pools and coral reefs to sample a part of this variety. As we might expect, the decomposers of the neritic zone are largely bacteria.

The *oceanic zone* is divided into three and sometimes four parts, all relatively poorly populated compared to the neritic zone. The *euphotic zone* consists of the waters into which sunlight penetrates, and extends down some 600 feet below the surface. Again, its producers are the phyto-plankton and its consumers the zooplankton and nekton. This vast area of the world's oceans is not one big region of constant abiotic features, for, outside an even light distribution, it experiences extreme temperature differences, both vertically and across its great longitudinal distances, and contains mighty ocean currents that determine the richness of the water's nutrients, its salinity and temperature, and thus the density of its phytoplankton, which in turn affects the quantity of zooplankton and nekton. In the euphotic zone, just as in other habitats, the forms have become specialized through utilizing its varied resources.

The rest of the oceanic zone receives no light and is divided into the *bathyal zone*—stretching from the bottom of the euphotic zone to a depth of about 6,000 feet—and the *abyssal zone*—all the sea below the bathyal; occasionally the term *hadal zone* is used to designate the perpetually cold and dark supreme depths of the oceanic trenches. These lower regions have been explored very little, although we know they contain life in the form of bizarre fish and arthropods who have successfully adapted to the great pressures of the lightless habitat. No producers exist in this ecosystem, as we know, only consumers and microconsumers or assimilators.

Fresh-water environments are also divided into two major categories, lotic and lentic habitats. *Lotic* communities are those living in relatively fast-running streams and brooks, *lentic* ones those in lakes or slow-running rivers. The classification depends on two conditions: current and the ratio of depth to surface area. Since lakes and ponds often contain currents or at least wave action and since streams often harbor quiet pools or calm backwaters, the difference between lotic and lentic waters is not very precise, but most stream-dwelling animals are clearly recognizable from their adaptations. Some develop suckers, hooks, or sticky body surfaces in order to cling to a solid substrate or to move across surfaces swept by currents; others possess streamlined body shapes. Behavior is also a clue; if an organism tends to face upstream or to press closely to surfaces, chances are it belongs to a lotic population.

Streams are usually relatively shallow and therefore have a large surface compared to their depth. These lotic waters are ordinarily well supplied with oxygen, with the result that most of their inhabitants are very sensitive to decreases in the oxygen content of the water produced by the discharge of wastes into creeks and rivers. Since streams also have extensive contacts with land, the major portion of their nutrients falls into the currents from their banks. Another large nutrient source for certain streams is the detritus washed in from lakes.

Lentic waters divide into three major zones (Fig. 32) that are similar to those of the marine habitats. The *littoral zone* adjoins the shore (and is thus the home of rooted plants) and extends down to a point called the *light compensation level,* or the depth at which the rate of photosynthesis equals the rate of respiration. The *limnetic zone* includes all the waters beyond the littoral zone and down to the light compensation level. Below that level is the *profundal zone.*

The animals of a lake or pond fall into the same categories as those in salt water: zooplankton, nekton, and benthos; an additional category, called the *periphyton,* consists of the forms living on the rooted plants.

The habitats of the continental land masses are naturally quite different from the aquatic habitats discussed above, most notably in their dearth of water; the distribution of this precious resource determines the habitability of particular geographic areas (compare a rain forest and a desert).

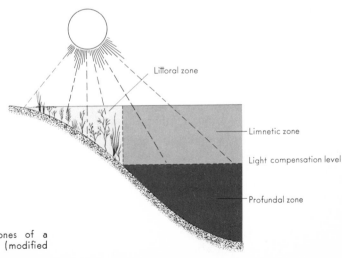

Fig. 32. Life zones of a fresh-water lake (modified from Odum).

Furthermore, as a whole, terrestrial habitats are more diverse than aquatic ones. The gaseous atmosphere is not as uniform a matrix for life as is the liquid hydrosphere, as the watery parts of the earth's surface are called. Hence, terrestrial habitats often show greater extremes, as of temperature, and sharper discontinuities, as on opposite sides of a mountain range, than are found in the ocean, for example.

Before we can understand why animals are distributed as they are, we must know something about the distribution of plants, for the animal consumers are dependent on the plant producers. The map in Fig. 33 shows both the major biomes of the continents and the major regions of animal habitation. A *biome* is the largest terrestrial ecological unit and is characterized by interactions of flora, fauna, and abiotic substances (the climate is considered to be part of the abiotic component). The biome takes its name from its climax or dominant plant form—a grass biome is an area in which grasslands predominate; a coniferous biome designates an area of cone-bearing evergreen trees, etc. The various zoogeographic areas contain more than one biome. The Australian region, for instance, contains a tropical scrub forest, a temperate and a tropical grassland, a temperate and a tropical deciduous forest, and chaparrals in which the climax vegetation consists of deciduous trees or shrubs with heavy evergreen leaves. Many of these same biomes are also found in South America.

The description, demarcation, and naming of the zoogeographical regions in Fig. 33 were largely the work of Alfred Russel Wallace, whom we have already mentioned in connection with the theory of natural selection. The first mammoth-sized step in defining these regions was to determine where each kind of animal lives and to observe its pattern of distribution—to note, for example, that deer live in North and South America and in Eurasia, that bears are found only in Eurasia and North America, that the great apes dwell in Central Africa and Southeast Asia, and that members of the camel family occur in Asia (and by domestication in North Africa) and South America (e.g., the llama). Wallace recorded a vast amount of this kind of information in his book, *The Geographical Distribution of Animals,* published in 1876. Working largely with mammals and birds, which were (and still are), zoogeographically speaking, the best-known forms, he concluded that the earth should be divided into six geographical zones, representing six areas of distinctive faunas.

In Fig. 34 is Wallace's summary of the distribution of vertebrate *families* and bird and mammal *genera* among the six zones. One striking fact appears: there are far more shared vertebrate families (shared by two or more zones) than there are peculiar, i.e., unshared, ones. In terms of families, then, the distinctions between the zones are rather negligible, but the number of bird and mammalian *genera* peculiar to each zone is quite significant. Undoubtedly, if Wallace, or any one else, could complete the gargantuan task of compiling this same information for species, the number of peculiar or unshared species would be most striking. However,

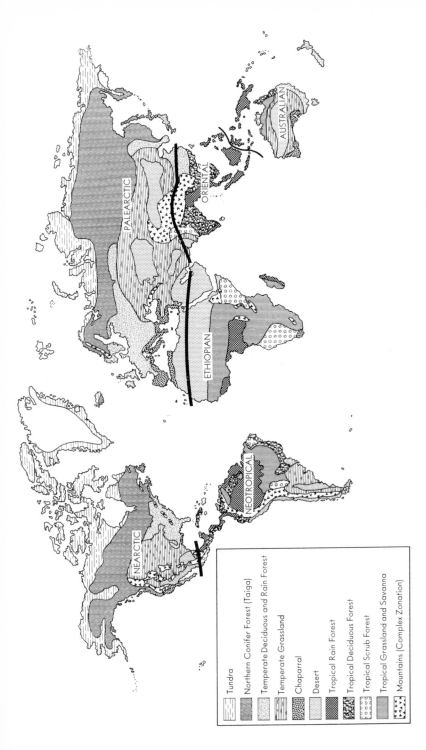

Fig. 33. A map showing the major biomes of the world (after Odum) and Wallace's six zoogeographical regions.

The map labels the following regions: NEARCTIC, NEOTROPICAL, PALEARCTIC, ETHIOPIAN, ORIENTAL, AUSTRALIAN.

Legend:

- Tundra
- Northern Conifer Forest (Taiga)
- Temperate Deciduous and Rain Forest
- Temperate Grassland
- Chaparral
- Desert
- Tropical Rain Forest
- Tropical Deciduous Forest
- Tropical Scrub Forest
- Tropical Grassland and Savanna
- Mountains (Complex Zonation)

on the basis of present data, faunistically these zones are most clearly distinguished at the generic level. Wallace's analysis was so carefully done that most zoogeographers today subscribe to his six zones.

Figure 34

Wallace's data on vertebrate families and mammalian and bird genera.

Regions	Vertebrates		Mammals			Birds		
	Total families	Unique families	Total genera	Unique genera		Total genera	Unique genera	
				Number	%		Number	%
Palaearctic	136	3	100	35	35	174	57	33
Ethiopian	174	22	140	90	64	294	179	60
Oriental	164	12	118	55	46	340	165	48
Australian	141	30	72	44	61	298	189	64
Neotropical	168	44	130	103	79	683	576	86
Nearctic	122	12	74	24	32	169	52	31

Three points are especially significant in this zonation. First, the zones do not coincide with the continental land masses. The *Palaearctic*, for example, includes North Africa along with Europe and northern Asia. Apparently the Sahara Desert and the Himalayas and their associated mountains are the chief barriers, since it is the Sahara that largely separates the Palaearctic from the Ethiopian, and the Himalayas, that separate the Palaearctic and the Oriental. Water barriers do divide zones, however—the Oriental from the Australian, the Palaearctic from the Nearctic, and the Nearctic from the Neotropical. Second, despite the barriers, at the generic level and above, the zones are very similar, indicating that certain forms are able to cross oceans, mountain ranges, and deserts. Third, certain animals (camels, for instance) live in widely separated places. This latter phenomenon can be explained by the fossil record.

Take the case of the camel, for example. Fossil camels have been found in North America, and, in fact, the earliest camel fossils are Nearctic, not Palaearctic or Neotropical, so we can reasonably conclude that camels arose in North America (but have since disappeared there) and spread to both Asia and South America where they became established and persist today. For this migration to have occurred, a land bridge must have joined Asia and North America, and fossil evidence supports the view that the Nearctic and Palaearctic zones were connected at various times in the Cenozoic.

Before leaving animal geography, we must mention *ecological equivalents*, those organisms that occupy essentially the same ecological niche in similar communities or even biomes but in different zoogeographical regions. These equivalents, significantly enough, need not be taxonomically related. Here, for instance, is a list of the grazing herbivores from four continents.

North America	Eurasia	South Africa	Australia
Bison	Saiga antelope	True antelopes	Large kangaroos
Pronghorn	Wild horse	Zebra	
Antelope	Wild ass		

Other equivalents are the jack rabbit of the western plains of North America and the capybara of the Argentine plains; the jack rabbit and capybara are members of different orders of mammals. Perhaps the most unusual equivalent mentioned here is that of the kangaroo compared to the other grazing herbivores. Kangaroos are being replaced now as Australian ranchers are introducing cattle and sheep, just as cattle and sheep have replaced pronghorn and bison in this country.

This ends our study of ecological zoogeography. We turn now to see whether our predictions concerning spatial diversity have been realized.

Our *first prediction* was that different animal forms represent different modes of living or, as we can now say, occupy different niches. How can we test this prediction? Let us start with the case of the flamingos. Since very similar forms were apparently exploiting the same niche, it might be thought they would constitute an exception to the prediction, but closer study revealed that the lesser flamingo species feeds on the producers in the lakes, the algae, while the greater flamingo species feeds on the primary consumers of the lake, the tiny benthic animals. These two different populations of birds thus exploit different niches. Our examination of the warblers revealed that they, too, do not compete for the same niche. Nowhere in nature, in fact, do two forms fill the same niche, for the good reason that if members of a given species compete with one another the species will suffer a decrease in population size (see p. 60).

The intense struggle that goes on *within* a species is unavoidable, since the members of the species, because of their genetic constitution, are very similar to one another, and thus they all exploit essentially the same niche. When two somewhat different forms occupy overlapping niches, however, they can capitalize on their differences and decrease all competition, except for the still unavoidable intrapopulation struggle, by evolving characters that reduce the overlap of the niches. Such a development is called *character displacement*, which only happens, of course, when the two populations involved are living together; where they dwell apart, these character differences are not emphasized. Each species, therefore, represents a unique way of life, or, as in the cases of character displacement, seems to be evolving such uniqueness.

In our *second prediction,* we said we would find distinctive and characteristic fauna, or at least mammals, on the separate continental land masses. This prediction has been only partly realized. The distinctive mammalian faunas coincide with continental boundaries only in a general way, for in Africa and Southeast Asia the main barriers are terrestrial and not aquatic ones. We see now that the words, "distinctive and characteristic fauna," are imprecise; we did not specify how distinct and unique a fauna we were expecting. From Wallace's data, we know that some genera are shared and some are unshared. There are enough unshared ones to enable us perhaps to argue convincingly that distinctions are present in the faunal zones, but if we compare the fauna at the family level, the prediction would not be fulfilled.

With this prediction, we have not, on the whole, made much progress. First, our chosen geographic areas did not turn out to be valid, although other recognizable geographic areas did. Second, we did not spell out carefully enough what we meant by "distinctive and characteristic fauna." If we had said distinctive and characteristic species, we still could not have tested the prediction, since comprehensive comparative data are not readily available. If we had specified genera, the results would have been generally favorable, since we could say we predicted what Wallace and others found. If we had specified families, the data would not really have supported the prediction. We should now discard the prediction as being not precisely formulated and realize, from hindsight, that six zoogeographical zones with certain unique genera and a very few unique families do exist and that such uniqueness or lack of it is related to problems of historical geography (recall the example of the camel and the Palaearctic-Nearctic Cenozoic land bridge).

Our *third prediction* stated that similar niches could be filled by organisms from different taxa. The existence of ecological equivalents demonstrates the validity of the prediction. As we saw, the larger Australian kangaroos live as grazing herbivores on the Australian grasslands, a niche filled by hoofed animals in other grassland biomes. Indeed the whole evolutionary adaptive radiation of marsupials (animals whose newborn young develop in a ventral pouch on the mother) in the Australian zone shows many cases of ecological equivalents to placental mammals (whose young develop attached to the internally borne placenta of the mother) of other zones. Examples are the marsupial Tasmanian wolf and the placental Holarctic wolves, the marsupial flying phalanger and the placental flying squirrels of other zones, and so forth. On a smaller scale, to cite another, famous example, the Galapagos finches—often called Darwin's finches—have evolved forms that exploit niches which are occupied on the mainland by such different birds as woodpeckers and flycatchers.

Ecological equivalents do not exist for all forms. For example, there is no equivalent in the Neotropical zone of the elephant or rhino of the Ethiopian zone, although savannah biomes are common to both zones.

The first and third predictions have been fully realized. The second prediction we are discarding because it is too vaguely stated to be carefully evaluated, even though we found it to be fulfilled in part. We can now conclude, therefore, that the kind of spatial diversity we would predict if animals have evolved is indeed the kind of diversity we find in nature today.

8

Phylogeny

We have now examined two parts of our proposal that evolution is an explanatory hypothesis for animal diversity. This chapter will be devoted to the third part, to testing the prediction that the animal taxa can be arranged in such a way as to represent a plausible evolutionary sequence or phylogeny.

As was true in the case of the other predictions, we must first compile a certain amount of background information before the prediction can be critically evaluated. Our immediate task is to take a careful look at the major animal taxa. Some we will examine in detail and others, of less phylogenetic importance, we will touch on only briefly. Because we have reason to believe that the evolutionary sequence is from simpler forms to more complex ones, we will start with the simpler phyla and progress to the more complicated groups.

For each major taxon, we will include a brief statement of its distinguishing anatomical features, followed by a short discussion of the significance of these features. The more important groups will be accompanied by a table containing information in some detail. Finally there will be a brief discussion of suspected evolutionary relationships, i.e., we will attempt to determine which group of living organisms most closely resembles the forms that are thought to be ancestral to the taxon under consideration. Such affinities, it will be recalled, are revealed by the study of homologies (see Chapter 3). We study the problem

71

this way for two reasons: (1) we do not have the space in this volume—or, indeed, in ten such volumes—to elucidate the phylogenetic relations of each and every species, and thus we must concentrate on a restricted number of taxa; and (2) we can more readily grasp the broad outlines and problems of phylogeny by studying the larger taxa.

Protozoa

The Protozoa are a heterogeneous group of unicellular animals or, as we prefer to call them, acellular animals. Their heterogeneity is most evident from an examination of the major subgroups. Usually the Protozoa are subdivided into classes on the basis of their mode of locomotion. We now know that this simple approach does not reflect the natural relationships within the group. Another grouping is suggested in Fig. 35. Its chief advantage is that it far more nearly approaches one aim of the modern systematist, i.e., that the groups be monophyletic, than does the taxonomy based on modes of locomotion.

The Radiolaria, Actinopoda, and the ameboid members of the Rhizoflagellata are commonly treated as a single group, the Sarcodina, because they all show some form of pseudopodia—protoplasmic extensions used for locomotion and food capture. This useful, though naive, classification must be changed in the light of modern principles of systematics, but we still do not know enough about the biology of these forms to know whether the alternative classification presented here is completely valid. For example, the Actinopoda contains two major subgroups, the Heliozoa and the Acantharia. These may have arisen from different groups within the yellow-green algae (Chrysophyta), and if so, the group Actinopoda is polyphyletic and should be split into two independent taxa.

The Rhizoflagellata are a large, diverse group. Both ameboid and flagellated forms are included in this grouping because certain forms are, strangely enough, both ameboid and flagellate. *Tetramitus rostratus* (Fig. 36) is an example. This tiny protozoan exists in two different forms. In one it possesses four slender, whip-like structures—the flagella—which are used for locomotion. In the other the flagella are absent, and blunt pseudopodia are present. The change from one form to the other takes place when there is simply a change in the salt concentration of the culture medium! Other forms within the rhizoflagellates, however, are exclusively ameboid—the amoeba itself (Fig. 14c) is a good example—or exclusively flagellate (Fig. 14d).

The Sporozoa are all parasitic forms and include such parasites as *Plasmodium* (Fig. 2c). Certain stages of the life cycle of some of them reveal flagellated gametes, hence their presumed relationship with the rhizoflagellates.

The Ciliophora (Fig. 14f) are probably the best-known group of protozoans. Although their cilia seem to be nothing more than short fla-

Figure 35

Major protozoan groups. (For illustrations see Fig. 14, Chap. 3.)

Groups	Distinguishing taxonomic features	Suspected affinities
Radiolaria	Siliceous skeleton; perforated central capsule; slender pseudopodia; usually of spherical shape; marine forms. Example: *Aulacantha, Acanthametra*	Pyrrophyta (a group of flagellated, usually photosynthetic algae)
Actinopoda	Skeleton occasionally siliceous but usually non-siliceous; no central capsule, or, when present, not perforated; pseudopodia (with central, slender rod) called axopodia; usually of spherical shape; marine and fresh-water forms. Example: *Actinospherium*	Chrysophyta (the yellow-green algae)
Rhizoflagellata	Ameboid or flagellated forms; ameboid forms with broad, blunt pseudopodia or slender ones, often forming a network; shells present in many forms; some forms multinucleate. Flagellate forms with one or more, occasionally several hundred, flagella, often containing many nuclei. Marine, fresh-water, and parasitic forms. Examples: *Amoeba, Coronympha*	Chrysophyta, but a group different from those related to the Actinopoda.
Sporozoa	All parasitic, showing a variety of body forms. Gametes of some flagellated. Example: Causative agent of malaria, *Plasmodium, Nosema*	Rhizoflagellata
Ciliophora	Commonly bilaterally symmetrical and covered with cilia, but with certain important exceptions; nuclear dimorphism; mouth; extensively differentiated cytoplasmic organelles which are mostly peripherally located. Examples: *Dileptus, Paramecium*.	Rhizoflagellata, a group different from those related to the Sporozoa.

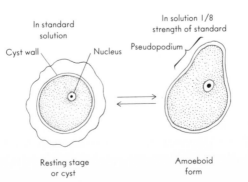
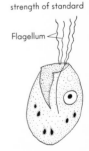

Fig. 36. Response of *Tetramitus rostratus* to different concentrations of salt solutions. (Modified from P. P. Grassé, ed., *Traité de Zoologie*. Paris: Masson et Cie 1952.)

In standard solution

Cyst wall

Nucleus

Resting stage or cyst

In solution 1/8 strength of standard

Pseudopodium

Amoeboid form

In solution 1/20 strength of standard

Flagellum

Flagellated form

gella, at least structurally, other characters clearly separate them from the rhizoflagellates. Their two most distinctive features are (1) their mode of asexual reproduction and (2) their nuclear dimorphism. Ciliates, as the Ciliophora are also called, undergo transverse fission during asexual reproduction (Fig. 37); the fission plane is at right angles to the long axis of the body. The zooflagellates, on the other hand, undergo longitudinal fission, as we have already noted. Nuclear dimorphism means that the ciliates possess one or more small diploid nuclei, called *micronuclei,* and one or more larger, usually polyploid nuclei called *macronuclei.* Other important characters are: a mouth or cytostome; differentiated cytoplasmic structures lying near the body surface such as muscle-like contractile fibrils; fibrils that supposedly perform a nerve-like function; and contractile *vacuoles,* which pump excess water from the ciliate's body.

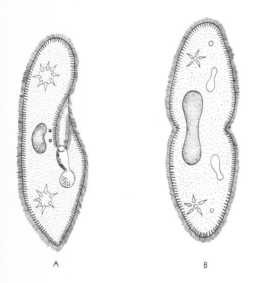

A   B

Fig. 37. Transverse fission in *Paramecium aurelia.* (A) Diagrammatic representation of a nondividing animal. (B) Dividing animal; compare with the photograph in Fig. 14F.

Since the protozoans are a polyphyletic group, we should abandon the term Protozoa as a taxonomic category. From here on, then, we shall use the term only as a common name, to refer collectively to acellular animals. But now how do we treat the groups formerly listed under the phylum Protozoa? There is no good answer to this as yet. The Radiolaria are easily separable from the Pyrrophyta, their most closely related forms, and might well be a phylum. Perhaps one large taxon could include the Actinopoda, rhizoflagellates, and Chrysophyta, since no clear differences exist between certain members of the former two groups and the yellow-green algae from which they probably arose. The Sporozoa could be included in the rhizoflagellates. The Ciliophora are so distinct that they deserve the status of a phylum along with the Radiolaria. These are some possible solutions, but obviously more systematic work is needed on this problem. Since the protozoa in all probability evolved from the algae (Fig. 35), their taxonomy can only be properly understood in conjunction with a taxonomic study of the algae.

In summary, the protozoa are acellular animals that show affinities not only to each other but to at least two groups of algae. They are undoubtedly a polyphyletic group. The arrangement of monophyletic groups presented here is consistent with modern taxonomic principles, but the taxonomic status of these proposed monophyletic groups is still unclear.

Porifera

The sponges are a large group of aquatic, sessile, filter feeders. They attach to a solid substratum in either fresh or salt waters and, using the flagella present in certain of their cells, force currents of water through their bodies (Fig. 38). From this water, they filter out particles of organic material which serve as their food. A single sponge consists of many cells, held together in very loose aggregates—so loose, in fact, that no real tissues are formed and the sponges are considered today as little more than integrated colonies of individual cells. The most characteristic cell type is the collared cell or choanocyte. This flagellated cell is similar to those found in certain zooflagellates. Largely for this reason, the sponges are thought to have evolved from colonies of choanocytic zooflagellates. The way certain sponges develop from the fertilized egg, on the other hand, is similar to the development of certain colonial green algae (Chlorophyta). These two lines of evidence suggest that either choanocytic zooflagellates or colonial green algae are ancestral to the sponges. In either case, it appears that the cellularized body of the sponges was achieved through the integration of a colony of either protozoan or algal organisms.

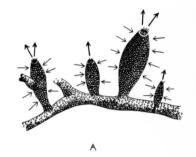

A

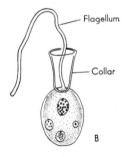

Flagellum

Collar

B

Fig. 38. (A) Diagrammatic representation of water currents around filter-feeding sponges. (B) A collar cell or choanocyte. (Redrawn from Buchsbaum.)

Platyhelminthes

The Platyhelminthes or flatworms are of the greatest importance to the problem of phylogeny. This phylum contains two classes of parasitic forms, the Trematoda and Cestoda, and one class of free-living forms. We are especially interested in this nonparasitic class, called the Turbellaria, which consists of bilaterally symmetrical, usually dorso-ventrally flattened worms ranging from a microscopic size up to several inches in length. The external body surface, or at least part of it, is typically covered with cilia. One midventral opening called a mouth serves for both the ingestion of food and the egestion of undigested matter. In all the free-living groups except one (Acoela), the mouth opens into a digestive cavity, which is also known as the gastrovascular cavity because it both digests and distributes the food to the body.

These worms are *hermaphroditic* or *monoecious,* that is, an individual can produce both eggs and sperm— but self-fertilization is the rare exception, not the rule. There are well-developed sexual organs. Except in the Acoela, nephridia are present in the free-living forms. *Nephridia* are excretory organs consisting of a tubule, which may be branched, leading exteriorly; interiorly the tubules may be closed (termed protonephridia) or open (metanephridia). In the Turbellaria, protonephridia are present (Fig. 39). Beyond these general similarities, Fig. 40 should be consulted for the characteristics of the four orders of flatworms we shall consider. The rhabdocoel and alloeocoel orders are not

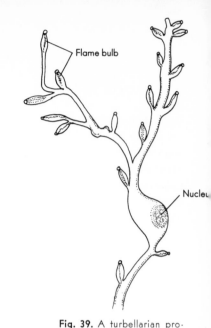

Fig. 39. A turbellarian protonephridium (redrawn from Hyman).

Figure 40

Major turbellarian platyhelminth taxa. (For illustrations see Fig. 13, Chap. 3.)

| | | MAJOR FEATURES | | | | | |
ORDERS	EXAMPLES	Symmetry	Body layers	Body cavities	Appendages	Special features	DEVELOPMENT CHARACTER
Acoela	*Convoluta, Amphiscolops*	Bilateral	Epicytium, ectocytium, and endocytium	None	None of general importance	Tiny, ciliated worm-like form	Internal fertilization, modified spiral cleavage, no larval forms
Rhabdocoela	*Polycystis, Catenula*	"	Partially cellularized epidermis, mesenchyme, and gastrodermis	"	"	Very small, ciliated worm-like form	Internal fertilization, spiral cleavage, no larval forms
Alloeocoela	*Geocentrophora, Monocelis*	"	"	"	"	Very small, partially ciliated, worm-like form	"
Tricladida	Planaria *(Dugesia)*	"	Extensive cellularization of epidermis, gastrodermis, and certain organ systems; mesenchyme largely syncytial	"	"	Small, ventrally ciliated, flattened, worm-like form	"
Polycladida	*Notoplana, Decodelus*	"	"	"	"	Small, ciliated, flattened, worm-like form	"

satisfactory taxonomic groups and are presently being revised. Since the new revisions would introduce unnecessary details for us, however, we shall ignore them here.

The first point to be noted about the Platyhelminthes is that the group is probably monophyletic. The parasitic forms presumably evolved from the free-living forms, and within the latter the relationships point to an acoeloid form as the ancestral form of the Turbellaria, and therefore of the flatworms as a whole.

The cell divisions of the flatworm zygote produce cleavages that orient the resultant cells into a definite spiral pattern; this type of development is termed spiral cleavage. Each cell in the spiral has a specific role to play in normal development. Certain ones form the outer or *epidermal layers* of the adult organism; certain others form the layer around the digestive cavity, the *gastrodermis;* one well-defined cell gives rise to all the structures lying between the epidermis and gastrodermis. This middle layer is the adult *mesoderm* or *mesenchyme,* which is a loosely organized mass of cells. Since the way organisms develop determines their form and since animal form is the essential subject of this book, let us review some of the basic concepts relating to animal development. The terms we shall use to describe the major parts of the embryo, called germ layers, and their derivative structures in the adult are shown in Fig. 41.

| | | | ORGAN SYSTEMS | | | | | | SUSPECTED |
estive	Reproductive	Muscular	Sensory and nervous	Excretory	Circulatory	Respiratory	Skeletal		AFFINITIES
ple ath, d uoles	Monoecious	Peripherally located contractile fibrils	Fibrils of so-called "nerve net"	None	None	None	None		Ciliophora or coelenterate planula
ath, rynx, estive ity	"	Muscle tissue, outer circular and inner longitudinal muscles plus others	Apparently true nervous tissue, plus sensory structures	Protonephridia	"	"	"		Acoela
ath, rynx, estive ity, ch have erticula	"	"	"	"	"	"	"		Acoela
ath, rynx, en probible), e- nched estive ity with erticula	"	"	"	"	"	"	"		Alloeocoela
ath, rynx, hly nched estive ity	"	"	"	"	"	"	"		Acoela

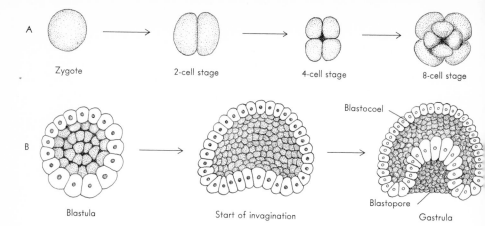

A Zygote → 2-cell stage → 4-cell stage → 8-cell stage

B Blastula → Start of invagination → Gastrula

Blastocoel

Blastopore

C **The germ layers and their derivative structures.**

Embryological tissue or germ layer	Derived adult structure	Position in adult
Ectoderm	Epidermis and associated structures	Outermost parts of the body, linings of the oral and anal ends of the digestive cavity
Endoderm	Gastrodermis	Lining of the digestive cavity except at the oral and anal ends
Mesoderm	(a) Mesenchyme—loosely connected mass of cells	Between epidermis and gastrodermis
	(b) Well-differentiated mesoderm—cells organized into tissues and organs	Between epidermis and gastrodermis

Fig. 41. Selected aspects of animal development. (A) Diagram of the first three divisions of the fertilized egg, with spiral cleavage apparent in the 8-cell stage. (B) Development of the hollow, spherical blastula into a gastrula by invagination. (Front half of the embryo is removed.) (C) Germ layers and their derivatives.

If we look carefully at the anatomy of the Acoela, we find that except for the germ cells—the eggs and sperm—the body is essentially syncytial, that is, there are no cell membranes separating the nuclei; the nuclei lie in a common cytoplasm. The differentiated structures, such as contractile fibrils, and the so-called nerves are differentiated cytoplasmic entities which contain no nuclei. The structures most nearly like true organs, i.e., those made up of cellularized tissues, are the reproductive structures. But even here true cellularization is absent.

This lack of cellularization in the soma (that part of the body exclusive of the germ cells) is usually interpreted to be a carry-over from an ancient, relatively simple type of organization. Some biologists have argued, however, that it is a derived simplicity, that Turbellaria at one time possessed an anal opening, in addition to the mouth, as part of their digestive system, but that the anus has now been lost. Those favoring this view of regressive evolution, as it has been called, think the Turbellaria were initially quite complex and therefore place them phylogenetically closer to other complex forms such as the segmented worms and arthropods. That the Turbellaria might have lost certain structures would make it difficult to determine their relationships to other groups except in a very general way. Those that espouse the first view, that the relative simplicity of the Acoela is not secondarily evolved, disagree about the form from which the acoels were evolved. Some believe that the general body form and cytoplasmic differentiations point to the ciliates, or more correctly to a ciliate-like form, as the most likely ancestor. But a larger number of researchers think the Acoela originated from the larva of the Cnidaria, the group that includes the jellyfish. To that group we now turn.

Cnidaria

Many biologists claim that the cnidarians or coelenterates are less complex than the flatworms, for two major reasons. First, for many years the cnidarians were thought to be diploblastic, to have bodies composed essentially of only two layers of protoplasm. All other cellularized animals, excluding the sponges, were termed triploblastic, because their bodies are formed from three layers of protoplasm. But more careful work shows that the coelenterates are really triploblastic, too. Between the outer epidermal layer of the body and the inner one surrounding the digestive or gastrovascular cavity, the gastrodermis, there is a jelly-like layer containing scattered cells that can be considered the third body layer, a kind of mesenchymal mesoderm. In the Cnidaria this layer is called the *mesoglea*. The second reason for thinking the cnidarians are less complex than the platyhelminths is the fact that they are radially (or biradially, in one class) symmetrical. Just why radial symmetry should be considered less complex than bilateral symmetry is not clear.

Since the first reason is no longer valid and the second reason is obscure, we have used our discretion and placed the Platyhelminthes before the Cnidaria, because there seems to be no form in the latter phylum as simple as the simplest turbellarian flatworms, i.e., the acoels. But there is a weakness in this position. The more complex Turbellaria, despite their syncytial characteristics, *are* probably more complex than the Cnidaria. However, since we must decide, we will emphasize the simplicity of the acoel flatworms rather than the complexity of certain other flatworms.

The Cnidaria are radially or biradially symmetrical animals with two major cellularized body layers, the outer epidermis and inner gastrodermis, and an intermediate layer of mesoglea. The number of cells in the mesoglea varies in each type of cnidarian. All members of the phylum possess tentacles that bear special cells, *cnidoblasts,* containing a special organelle, the *nematocyst* (Fig. 42). The nematocyst is capable of explosively discharging a thread-like tube armed with barbs and loaded with a poison. This characteristic armament of the cnidarians is used to im-

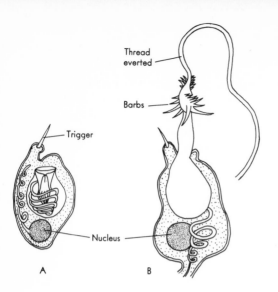

Fig. 42. Coelenterate cnidoblasts. (A) Nematocyst undischarged; (B) nematocyst discharged. (Redrawn from Buchsbaum.)

mobilize prey and can cause painful, occasionally fatal, injuries to humans who come in contact with certain kinds of jellyfish.

Three classes are recognized in this phylum (Fig. 43). Of the two main body forms found in the Cnidaria—the *polyp* and the *medusa*—the class Hydrozoa shows both, the class Scyphozoa essentially only the medusa, and the class Anthozoa only the polyp. The polyp is basically a cylinder; one end is attached to the substratum and the other contains a mouth surrounded by tentacles. The medusa is a free-swimming form and, compared to the polyp, is a cylinder much compressed along its central axis (Fig. 44). The hydrozoan polyp is distinguishable from the anthozoan polyp because it has radial symmetry (instead of biradial symmetry) and lacks *septa*-vertical gastrodermal ridges extending into the gastrovascular cavity. The hydrozoan medusa is distinguishable from the scyphozoan medusa by the presence of a *velum*, an inward extension of the outer margin of the jellyfish bell or umbrella (see Fig. 44).

Figure 43

Major cnidarian taxa. (For illustrations see Fig. 12, Chap. 3.)

| | | MAJOR FEATURES | | | | | |
CLASSES	EXAMPLES	Symmetry	Body layers	Body cavities	Appendages	Special features	DEVELOPMEN CHARACTEF
Hydrozoa	*Hydra*	Radial	Epidermis, mesoglea, gastrodermis	None	Tentacles	Stinging cells	Internal and external fertilization, indeterminat cleavage, planula
Scyphozoa	*Aurelia, Rhizostomum*	"	Epidermis, cellular mesoglea, gastrodermis	"	"	"	"
Anthozoa	Stony coral (*Astrangia*), *Baloceroides*	Biradial	Epidermis, highly cellular mesoglea, gastrodermis	"	"	"	"

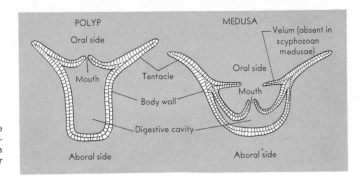

Fig. 44. Typical coelenterate body forms: tranverse sections of polyp and medusa (the latter is inverted for the sake of comparison).

In all the classes, the larval form produced from sexual processes is called the *planula,* which is a completely ciliated, solid mass of cells. In those forms that have only a hydroid stage in their life cycle (certain hydrozoans and anthozoans), the planula settles to the bottom, attaches at one end, and develops a mouth and tentacles at the other end. In those forms with only medusae, the planula develops into a medusa directly. In certain hydrozoans, both medusa and polyp are present in a life cycle. Here the planula develops into a polyp which then buds off medusae by an asexual process. These medusae in turn produce the gametes that form, upon fertilization, the zygote which develops into a new planula, thus completing the life cycle (Fig. 45).

Biologists disagree about the origin of the Cnidaria and the interrelations of the cnidarian classes. Some think that the Anthozoa contain the more primitive members of the phylum and that the Hydrozoa are the most specialized. Others assert just the reverse. Proponents of the first view believe that the Cnidaria originated from bilaterally symmetrical Turbellaria and that the biradial symmetry of the anemones and their kin is one consequence of this parentage. The development of a sessile mode of life led to radial symmetry and structures (such as mesoglea, for example) no longer needed by the increasingly inactive animals were reduced in size or eliminated. The other school of thought believes that

| | | | ORGAN SYSTEMS | | | | | SUSPECTED |
	Reproductive	Muscular	Sensory and nervous	Excretory	Circulatory	Respiratory	Skeletal	AFFINITIES
h, ive	Monoecious and dioecious	Muscle fibers in bases of epidermal and gastrodermal cells	"Nerve net" and sensory cells	None	None	None	None	Colonial green algae (Chlorophyta) or anthozoan
	Dioecious	"	"	"	"	"	"	Trachyline hydrozoan or anthozoan
	Dioecious or monoecious	"	"	"	"	"	Exo- and endoskeletons in corals	Trachyline hydrozoan or turbellarian

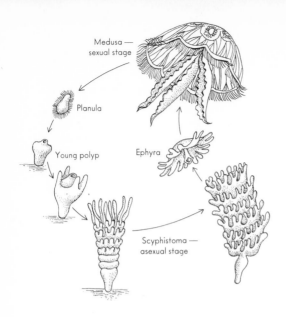

Fig. 45. Metagenesis or alteration of generations in *Aurelia* (redrawn from Buchsbaum).

a medusa is the more primitive body form and thinks that the present-day Cnidaria evolved from a hydrozoan in which the planula develops into medusa-like form, called the *actinula*. The actinula can develop (1) into medusae, or (2) upon attachment, into polyps that will then produce medusae, or (3) into polyps from which no medusae are produced. In this way, the various classes of cnidarians with their typical body forms were evolved. The adherents to this second viewpoint argue that the planula is the primitive coelenterate form which preceded the actinula, and they have suggested that the planula evolved from a spherically shaped colony of green algae (Chlorophyta).

Nemertina

We have not mentioned this group before, but it is important because it contains worm-like forms that show two features not encountered in the organisms considered thus far. The first feature is the presence of two openings, a mouth and an anus, in the digestive system. This structure is an advantageous specialization because it enables the ingested food to move in just one direction in the gut. Partially digested and undigestible particles are not mixed, and the gut itself can readily evolve specializations along its length for digestion. Such specializations are not present in the simpler nemertines, only in the more complex ones. The other special feature of the nemertines is the presence of a circulatory system. In addition to the muscular and coordinative elements in the Cnidaria and flatworms, the nemertines possess excretory structures (as do the flatworms, too) and also this circulatory system for transporting substances throughout the body.

The nemertines, in brief, are smallish, bilaterally symmetrical worms, a few inches in length, that are covered externally with cilia. All possess an extensible *proboscis* or tube that lies dorsally in the anterior end of the body and is used for capturing food. Like the flatworms and cnidarians, the body contains no cavities other than the digestive one. Spiral cleavage is present in the early stages of development. Most workers think the Nemertina are closely related to the flatworms.

Aschelminthes

Although this phylum contains an array of forms that are related in many respects, it may not be a monophyletic group. We consider them here because they show an anatomical feature not seen in the phyla already discussed. This new feature is the *pseudocoel*, a cavity that lies between the gastrodermis and the outer body wall. Since this body wall is composed internally of mesoderm and externally of epidermis, and has a cuticle on the very outside, the pseudocoel is a body cavity lined with gastrodermis and mesoderm. It develops out of a cavity, known as a blastocoel (see Fig. 41), found in the early embryonic stages. In the Nematoda, the largest and perhaps the most important class in this phylum, the pseudocoel in adults contains reproductive organs. The body wall houses the other specialized organ systems. Spiral cleavage is present in the Aschelminthes. The affinities of the Aschelminthes to other groups are not well known. The best guess is that they are distantly related to the free-living flatworms.

Annelida

The outstanding anatomical feature of the annelid worms is their segmentation. In an ideally segmented animal, all the segments of the body would be identical, but such a situation is never found, for segments often have some special function. For example, the head segment or segments and the segment containing the anus will naturally be different from each other and from other segments. The differences between segments that are shown by all segmented animals can arise through fusion or through the loss of segments, or by changes in the organs within a segment. The annelids are as ideally segmented as any living form, but even they show many intersegmental differences. In external anatomy, the differences between segments are most obvious at the anterior end; internally, they are largely in the anterior part of the digestive, nervous, and circulatory systems, and the gonads are localized in certain segments.

In addition to segmentation, another important aspect of the annelids is their mode of larval development. The fertilized egg undergoes spiral cleavage of the sort seen in the flatworms. And, as in the flatworms, the cells formed by cleavage develop into specific parts of the adult, but before the adult stage is reached, a typical larval form appears which is called the *trochophore* (Fig. 52). This larval form is also found in the

Mollusca, the next phylum to be discussed. The development of the mesoderm in the trochophore is of interest here. As is typical of spiral cleavage, the mesodermal cells are all derived from the division products of a single cell. In the trochophore, the mesodermal cells lie against the ectoderm and endoderm and create a hollow space between them that is called the *coelom* (Fig. 46). This method of coelom formation, in which the mesodermal cells are separated into linings of the epi- and gastro-dermis, is termed *schizocoelous*.

The cavity thus formed is of considerable importance in the re-maining phyla and especially so for the annelids. All annelids possess a well-developed coelom, which, as we have just seen, is formed within and entirely surrounded by mesoderm or its derivative tissues. (Compare this with the pseudocoel, p. 83.) In the Annelida, the coelom contains a fluid and the various organs which protrude into it from the body or gut wall. In other phyla, the coelom is often completely filled with a

Fig. 46. Annelid development and body structure. (A) Development of mesoderm. (B) A trochophore larva. (C) Cross section of an earthworm body. (All redrawn from Buchsbaum.)

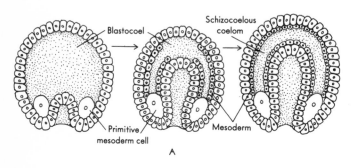

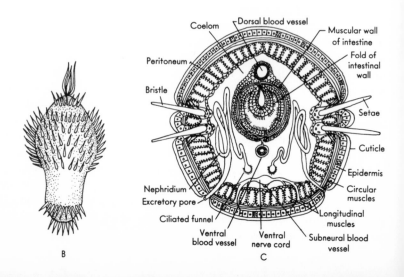

variety of organs and tissues. The fluid in the annelid coelom serves as a necessary liquid internal environment and also as a sort of skeleton— a "hydraulic skeleton," as it has been called. Contraction of the circular muscles in the body wall (Fig. 46) produces a turgor or pressure in the fluid that forces the body to elongate, while contraction of the longitudinal muscles builds up a turgor pressure that expands the body.

Figure 47 reveals that the annelids possess all the major organ systems except those for respiration. This of course does not mean that annelids do not respire. All living things breathe and annelids are no exception. The point is that the annelids have no organ system specifically designed for respiratory purposes. Gaseous exchanges occur largely through capillaries in the parapodia of polychetes and through the body surface of the forms in the other two classes. Metanephridia (see p. 76) take care of excretion.

The three classes of annelids shown in the table probably form a monophyletic group. The origins of the most primitive group, the polychetes, are very obscure. The best guess, and it is not much more than that, is that these annelids arose from free-living flatworms some time in the Pre-Cambrian.

Mollusca

The molluscs are soft-bodied forms that possess a shell or at least a modified shell. The shell can be considered as a kind of skeleton and is formed by the animals themselves. In most molluscs it is a conspicuous, externally borne structure, as in clams and snails. In squids it is an internal structure. A large muscular "foot," or thickening of the ventral body wall, appears in nearly all molluscs. In the most complex ones, the cephalopods, the foot is greatly modified into a crown of tentacles surrounding the head.

The primitive molluscs were undoubtedly segmented, but most of the present-day forms have lost this character. The class Amphineura contains the only living molluscs that show segmentation. These chitons, as they are called, have an eight-sectioned shell, but internally give little evidence of segmentation. In 1952 Danish scientists dredged up from an ocean depth of about 10,000 feet an amphineuran mollusc, *Neopilina,* which gives clear evidence of internal segmentation, although it has but a single shell. This exciting discovery establishes direct evidence of segmentation in the lower molluscs and is a fascinating example of "living fossils," so named because other members of its subtaxon within the Amphineura are known only from Ordovician fossils!

The coelom of molluscs is much reduced. It is most easily seen as the cavity around the heart. A *hemocoel,* however, is present, and since it, like the nematode pseudocoel, arises from the embryonic blastocoel, its development is different from that of the coelom, which develops within the mesoderm. But the hemocoel is unlike the pseudocoel in that

Figure 47

Major annelid taxa. (For illustrations see Fig. 9, Chap. 3.)

| CLASSES | EXAMPLES | MAJOR FEATURES | | | | | DEVELOPMEN CHARACTE |
		Symmetry	Body layers	Body cavities	Appendages	Special features	
Polycheta	Clam worm (Nereis), Eunice	Bilateral	Epidermis, differentiated mesoderm, gastrodermis	Coelom (schizocoelus)	Parapodia with setae	Segmented worm-like body	External fer lization, spi cleavage, trochophore larva
Oligocheta	Earthworm (Lumbricus)	"	"	"	Setae	"	External fer lization, spi cleavage, direct developmen
Hirudinea	Medicinal leech (Hirudo)	"	"	"	None (with one exception)	"	"

it is eventually enclosed in mesoderm (as is the coelom). Its developmental history, therefore, is what most clearly distinguishes it from the coelom. In the molluscs, the hemocoel functions as part of the circulatory system. Blood leaves the heart and passes through arteries that terminate in the cavities or sinuses of the hemocoel. The blood is collected again from these sinuses by veins and returned to the heart. The early stages of molluscan development are very similar to those of annelids, since spiral cleavage and the trochophore larva are both present.

Figure 48

Major molluscan taxa. (For illustrations see Fig. 10, Chap. 3.)

| CLASSES | EXAMPLES | MAJOR FEATURES | | | | | DEVELOPMEN CHARACTE |
		Symmetry	Body layers	Body cavities	Appendages	Special features	
Amphineura	Chiton, Neopilina	Bilateral	Epidermis, differentiated mesoderm, gastrodermis	Coelom (Schizocoelous) and hemocoel	None of taxonomic significance	Soft body with shell and "foot"	External fer lization, spi cleavage, trochophore larva
Gastropoda	Snail (Helix)	"	"	"	"	"	Internal fer lization, spi cleavage, di developmen larval form, trochophore and veliger larvae in ma rine forms
Pelecypoda	Oyster (Ostrea), Clam (Schizothaerus)	"	"	"	"	"	External fer lization, spi cleavage, trochophore then veliger larvae in marine form glochidium larva in fres water forms
Cephalopoda	Octopus (Octopus)	"	"	"	Tentacles	"	Internal fer lization, spi cleavage, no conspicuous larval stage

tive	Reproductive	Muscular	ORGAN SYSTEMS	Excretory	Circulatory	Respiratory	Skeletal	SUSPECTED AFFINITIES
			Sensory and nervous					
h, ive anus	Dioecious	Outer circular and inner longitudinal	Ventral nerve cord (with segmented ganglia) and anterior brain	Meta-nephridia	Large dorsal and ventral vessels, and heart	No specialized structures	None, except for so-called "hydraulic skeleton"	Turbellarian flatworms (?)
	Monoecious	"	"	"	"	"	"	Polycheta
	"	"	"	"	"	"	"	Oligocheta

The major molluscan classes are listed in Fig. 48. As we can see, they are best differentiated on the basis of their shell (Fig. 10). Excretion is handled by a specialized organ, the *kidney*. For our purposes, a kidney is an organ composed of many nephridia. For the first time, we find well-defined respiratory organs, the *gills*. These gills vary considerably in form from one group to another and are completely absent in certain land snails, where lung-like structures take their place. The similarity in the early development of the molluscs and annelids and the evidence of segmentation in both suggest a relationship between them. Perhaps they had a common ancestor in a segmented, flatworm-like creature.

tive	Reproductive	Muscular	ORGAN SYSTEMS	Excretory	Circulatory	Respiratory	Skeletal	SUSPECTED AFFINITIES
			Sensory and nervous					
h, ive anus	Dioecious	Complex musculature, especially muscular foot	Well developed with ganglia and brain	Kidneys	Heart, vessels, and hemocoel	Gills	Dorsal shell, segmented	Annelida or turbellarian flatworm as common ancestor of both annelids and molluscs
	Monoecious	"	"	"	"	"	Dorsal, spiral shell sometimes much reduced or absent	Amphineuran-like form
	Dioecious	"	"	"	"	"	Bivalve shell	"
	"	Complex musculature, foot of other classes here highly modified	Well developed with ganglia, brain, and well-developed eye	"	"	"	Hard internal structures often much reduced, occasionally absent	"

Onychophora

This small phylum contains forms of considerable significance to the phylogeny of segmented animals. The onychophorans are terrestrial forms with soft, bilaterally symmetrical, segmented bodies; a pair of legs is on each segment (Fig. 49), and the legs carry a set of claws that is similar to those in insects. The outermost layer of the body is a thin cuticle, underneath which is a body wall with muscles organized in circular and longitudinal layers, as in annelids. Another important feature is the presence of *tracheae,* respiratory organs that open externally through special structures, the *spiracles,* and that extend internally into the body tissues as delicate tubes. The coelom is well developed in young onychophorans, but is almost obliterated in the adult where a hemocoel is the prominent body cavity. The development of the fertilized egg is similar to arthropod development, which we shall come to shortly.

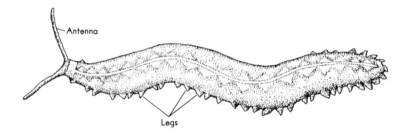

Fig. 49. A peripatus *(Macroperipatus geayi)* found in the leaf mold of tropical rain forests (from Buchsbaum).

Members of this phylum are found in damp leaf mold or rotting logs in Australia, southern Asia, Africa, and South and Central America, which suggests that in the past they were a very widespread form.

The segmentation of the body and the organization of the body muscles indicate that some annelid-like form might have been an ancestor of the onychophorans. But the absence of annelid-like development argues against this. The Onychophora may have arisen from a group of segmented worms, now extinct, that was different from those which gave rise to the present-day annelids and molluscs.

Arthropoda

This phylum contains the largest number of species and is universally characterized by a segmented body that bears jointed appendages and is enclosed in a hard *exoskeleton.* The arthropod body is divided into highly specialized segments that are greatly different from one another. The arthropodan head is the result of the fusion of six segments. The rest of the body may or may not be divisible into parts (thorax, abdomen, etc.).

The exoskeleton is an outer layer or *cuticle* composed essentially of a material called *chitin*, which is secreted by the arthropod epidermis. This chitinous exoskeleton is so rigid that it serves as a stable site for the attachment of muscles. To appreciate the difference between this type of exoskeleton and a chordate endoskeleton like our own bony skeleton, let us imagine ourselves in a suit of medieval armor. If we were to remove our bones and attach the muscles, formerly attached to the bones, to the inside of the armor, the arrangement would resemble the structure in the arthropods. The exoskeleton is a protective armor and

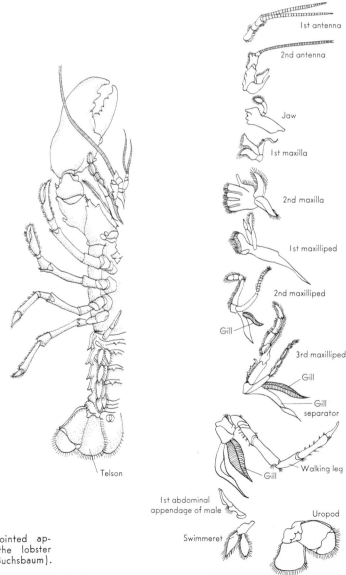

Fig. 50. The jointed appendages of the lobster (redrawn from Buchsbaum).

a frame for the muscles, but it poses a problem in growth. Just as a person enclosed in armor can grow no larger than the limits imposed by the armor, so an arthropod is limited in size by its exoskeleton. Arthropods overcome this restriction by periodically *molting*, that is, they shed their old hard exoskeleton and take on a new soft one. Its softness offers no effective resistance to muscle action and thus makes efficient movement difficult. The arthropod grows, although the exoskeleton soon hardens again and limits further growth until the next molt.

The jointed appendages of arthropods appear in a fascinating variety of forms that is matched by the equally interesting array of functions they perform. A good example is the lobster (Fig. 50). The lobster's appendages are *biramous*, i.e., have two branches, and the branches are variously specialized in the different appendages. Other forms such as the centipedes and millipedes have many appendages for locomotion that are all alike. But in the head region of these latter forms, the appendages are modified into sensory and ingestory structures.

Development in the arthropods begins with the fertilization of an egg containing a large amount of yolk. This yolk prevents the cleavage furrow from passing through the egg; the furrows can penetrate only the surface of the egg in a process called superficial cleavage. The presence of the yolk and its resultant superficial cleavage lead to later development that is peculiar in many respects to the arthropods. Some biologists, however, believe the mode of formation of the mesoderm is a modification of that found in spiral cleavage. In crustaceans, there is usually a distinct

Figure 51

Major arthropod taxa. (For illustrations see Fig. 8, Chap. 3.)

CLASSES	EXAMPLES	MAJOR FEATURES					
		Symmetry	Body layers	Body cavities	Appendages	Special features	DEVELOPMEN CHARACTE
Chelicerata	Black-widow spider (*Latrodectus*), Horse-shoe crab (*Xiphosura*)	Bilateral	Epidermis, differentiated mesoderm, gastrodermis	Coelom hemocoel reduced	Jointed, 4 pair on cephalo-thorax for locomotion	Segmented body with exoskeleton	Usually inte nal fertiliza tion, super-ficial cleava direct devel ment
Crustacea	Fiddler Crab (*Uca*), Lobster (*Homarus*), Shrimp (*Stenopus*)	"	"	"	Jointed, su-perficially 1 pair per segment, diverse functions	"	Internal or ternal fertil tion, usuall superficial cleavage, us ally nauplit larva
Myriapoda	Centipede (*Scolopendra*), Millipede (*Spirobolus*)	"	"	"	Jointed, many for locomotion along length of body	"	Internal fe zation, supe ficial cleava direct devel ment
Insecta	Honeybee (*Apis*), Swallowtail butterfly (*Papilio*)	"	"	"	Jointed, 3 pair for locomotion on thorax, plus wings on most	"	Internal fe zation, supe ficial cleava often a serie of larval mc

larval form, the *nauplius*. In the insects, development of the zygote leads to larval molts that may achieve little or much change in body form, depending on the species. The change from a caterpillar to a butterfly is an example of extreme change (see Fig. 26).

The four different classes of arthropods (Fig. 51) are most easily recognized by the appendages and their location on the body (see Fig. 8). The body of the Chelicerata has two parts, an anterior cephalothorax and a posterior abdomen. The adult appendages all arise from the cephalothorax, and, typically, there are four pairs of walking legs. In the Crustacea, the body is also divisible into cephalothorax and abdomen, and a pair of biramous appendages is generally found on each segment. We have already discussed these (see Fig. 50). The Myriapoda characteristically have many pairs of walking legs, but not as many as the "hundred" and "thousand" implied by the names centipede and millipede. The insect body has three major parts, the head, thorax, and abdomen. The thorax usually has three pairs of legs and a pair or two of wings. The claws on the walking legs are similar to the onychophoran claws.

The affinities of arthropods seem fairly clear in one respect only; the Crustacea and the Chelicerata, along with the now extinct trilobites (see p. 46), form a fairly distinct group, and the Myriapoda and Insecta form another distinct group. Indeed, one line of modern thought holds that perhaps these two large groups have had separate evolutionary origins, the first from some ancient annelid-like form and the second from an onychophoran-like form (which in turn may be related to a now extinct type of segmented worm). If this is so, then there are some striking convergences in the arthropods. Two examples: (1) the tracheae of the spiders (Chelicerata) must have had a separate evolutionary origin

estive	Reproductive	Muscular	ORGAN SYSTEMS Sensory and nervous	Excretory	Circulatory	Respiratory	Skeletal	SUSPECTED AFFINITIES
uth, estive e, anus	Usually dioecious	Well developed	Paired, ventral nerve cord with segmental ganglia and anterior brain	Malpighian tubules	Dorsal heart vessels, and hemocoel	Gill books, lung books, and tracheae	Chitinous exoskeleton	Ancient annelid-like form (?)
	Dioecious	"	"	Green glands or Malpighian tubules	"	Gills	"	Ancient aquatic Chelicerata (?)
	Dioecious	"	"	Malpighian tubules	"	Tracheae	"	Onychophoran-like form
	Dioecious	"	"	Malpighian tubules	"	Tracheae	"	"

from that of the onychophorans, myriapods, and insects; (2) the special excretory organ of many arthropods, the Malpighian tubules, must also have been evolved twice, independently of each other. And, if we accept these affinities, it means that the arthropods are not monophyletic but diphyletic and that this group should undergo certain taxonomic revisions.

Lophophorate phyla

This somewhat enigmatic group of three phyla has in common the possession of a *lophophore,* a tentacle-bearing extension of the body used for feeding, and certain general features such as a coelom. Beyond this, they are highly diverse. The Brachiopoda, which we encountered in our study of the fossil record, are of interest because they produce a larva that can be interpreted as a trochophore, and thus they show an affinity to the polychaete annelids. The Brachiopoda also have a type of mesoderm formation that is found in the starfish and chordates, groups we must consider in the next sections.

Echinodermata

The echinoderms are pentaradiate, coelomate, marine organisms with an endoskeleton of calcareous plates that often have spines protruding externally. Their most unique character is a *water-vascular system,* which is an arrangement of tubes that lies internally around the mouth and that has side branches passing along the inside of the body wall. These branches connect through the body wall with the externally placed *tube feet* (Fig. 52). By controlling the water pressure in this system of tubes, the echinoderm can make the end of the tube feet convex or concave. When the tube foot is placed against a substratum and a con-

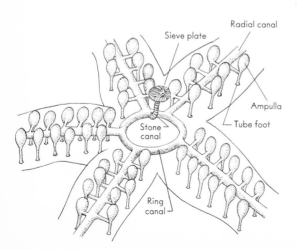

Fig. 52. Diagram of the water vascular system in the starfish (redrawn from Buchsbaum).

cavity is produced, the end of the foot acts as a suction cup. The suction is released when the end of the foot becomes convex. By attaching and releasing the tube feet as they extend and contract, the echinoderms are able to move around.

The development of the echinoderms reveals a bilaterally symmetrical larval form, the *bipinnaria*. The coelom of the larva is formed when pouches are pinched off from the larval endoderm (Fig. 53). Note that this enterocoelous method of mesoderm formation is quite different from the schizocoelous method associated with the coelomate forms that show spiral cleavage. (The brachiopods also show this enterocoelous method.) The bilateral, echinoderm bipinnaria larva, with its coelomic pouches, develops through a striking series of changes into the pentaradiate adult form.

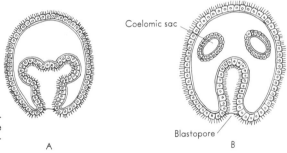

Coelomic sac

Blastopore

A   B

Fig. 53. Mesoderm formation in echinoderms and the formation of the enterocoelous coelom.

The affinities of the echinoderms to other invertebrates are, at best, obscure. Their adult form, with its pentaradiate symmetry and water-vascular system, represents an unusual and distinctive group of animals. The larva, with its enterocoelous mode of mesoderm formation, is unique among the forms we have thus far studied. Since nothing definite can be said about the origins of the echinoderms, further comments will be deferred until we discuss the problem of the origins of the major taxa.

Chordata

We come finally to the phylum to which we ourselves belong. The chordates are bilaterally symmetrical, segmented forms characterized by a notochord and its associated endoskeleton, a dorsal, hollow nerve tube, and gill slits. The *notochord* is a dorsal, rod-like structure that is present in young and adults of certain simpler chordates, but only in the embryos of higher chordates. In the higher chordates, the vertebrates, it is replaced during embryogenesis with the vertebrae; the notochord's position in the body is taken by the segmented backbone. Along with the appearance of the vertebrae, of course, the rest of the bony endoskeleton appears.

The *dorsal nerve tube* develops when the embryonic epidermis or ectoderm is infolded and pinched off. The tube becomes, through development, the central nervous system, and the anterior end greatly enlarges to form the brain. Note especially the dorsal position of the nerve tube, since in the major invertebrate phyla—the annelids, molluscs, and arthropods—the position of the major nerve trunk is ventral.

The *gill slits*, the third major chordate character, are present, like the notochord, only in the simpler chordate taxa and in the embryonic stages of the more complex forms. In humans they appear as nonfunctional gill clefts in the very young embryos. The embryonic muscle masses in the vertebrate embryos also give clear evidence of segmentation. This, plus the segmentation evident in the backbone, are two obvious indications of segmentation in the chordates.

The chordate coelom is well developed and is typically packed with various organs. The organs in this cavity have space for development, are well protected, and are lubricated, so to speak, with coelomic fluids which enable them to be in contact with one another and yet not hinder the motions of the animal body. This coelom is an enterocoelous one, like that of echinoderms and brachiopods.

Our breakdown of the chordate taxa is more complicated than that of any of the previous classes (Fig. 54). The first question is why the sea-squirts or Tunicata are included in this phylum. To answer, we must

Figure 54

Major chordate taxa. (For illustrations see Fig. 7, Chap. 3.)

| SUB-PHYLUM | SUPER CLASS | CLASS | EXAMPLES | MAJOR FEATURES | | | | | |
				Symmetry	Body layers	Body cavities	Appen-dages	Special features	SUSI AFF
Tunicata			Sea-squirt (*Ciona*)	Bilateral	Epidermis, differentiated mesoderm, gastrodermis	Coelom (entero-coelous)	None	Body with head, trunk, and tail in larva; endo-skeleton	Echinc (?), pri worms
Vertebrata	Pisces		Trout (*Salvelinus*), Angler fish (*Antennarius*)	"	"	"	Fins	Body with head, trunk, and tail; endo-skeleton	Ancien which from t larva
	Tetrapoda	Amphibia	Grass frog (*Rana*)	"	"	"	Two pair	"	Devon
		Reptilia	Garter snake (*Thaiunoplus*)	"		"	"	"	Mississ or Penns amphi
		Aves	Pigeon (*Columba*)	"	"	"	"	"	Early Mesoz reptile
		Mammalia	Dog (*Canis*) Man (*Homo*)	"	"	"	"	"	"

look at the larval tunicates. Since all three chordate characters are in evidence in these forms, the tunicates must be listed in the phylum Chordata. The adult tunicates represent an adaptation to a sessile, filter-feeding life and thus have had no selective pressure to evolve an elaborate skeleton or nervous system. Therefore, they have preserved the gill slits as a filter apparatus and have only a very simple nervous system and no endoskeleton. The remaining groups, all appearing in the subphylum Vertebrata, have been mentioned in various contexts throughout this volume, especially in the discussions of the fossil record. There we spoke of a progressive scale of complexity, starting with the fishes and going up through the amphibians and reptiles to the birds and mammals. Note the changes in the heart listed in Fig. 54—a good example of increasing anatomical complexity. A study of the brain would reveal the same progression, as would a comparison of the kidneys, at least in certain respects.

The affinities of these taxa, except for the tunicates, are perhaps the clearest of any studied yet. We have good fossil evidence of the tetrapods that tells us a great deal about when and how the various groups arose. We have less clear evidence about the origin of the fishes; some biologists have recently argued that the fishes originated from an early Paleozoic larval tunicate. But where the tunicates came from we do not know.

Various theories have been put forward for the origin of chordates in general. Annelids and certain chelicerate arthropods have been proposed as hypothetical ancestral forms. But then the major puzzle is how the ventral nerve cord got into the dorsal chordate position. One sugges-

PMENTAL ACTERS	Digestive	Reproductive	Muscular	ORGAN SYSTEMS Sensory and nervous	Excretory	Circulatory	Respiratory	Skeletal
al fertili- entero- s, unique e-shaped	Mouth, digestive tract, anus	Monoecious	Present but relatively simple	Present as dorsal tube in larva	No special structures	Simple heart and vessels	Gills	Endoskeleton, notochord
al ation, coelous	"	Dioecious	Well developed	Dorsal tube with brain	Kidney	Closed system with 2-chambered heart	"	Endoskeleton, notochord in embryo, cartilaginous or bony skeleton in adult
al ation	"	"	"	"	"	Closed system with 3-chambered heart	Gills in embryos	Endoskeleton, notochord in embryo, bony skeleton in adult
al ation	"	"	"	"	"	Closed system with 3–4-chambered heart	"	"
	"	"	"	"	"	Closed system with 4-chambered heart	"	"
	"	"	"	"	"	"	"	"

tion is that the animals simply turned over—thus reversing the ventral and dorsal surfaces, but this possibility would involve such a drastic evolutionary change that it is probably not valid. If nothing else, these theories show how unlikely it is that a highly complex group like the chordates evolved from other equally complex groups.

Perhaps a more profitable approach is to return to the less complex forms. Two possibilities present themselves. Early echinoderm and early chordate development are very similar—in their mode of mesoderm and coelom formation, for example—and, unlikely as it seems from comparing adult forms, these parallels in embryonic development suggest that the two groups had a common ancestor. The second possibility is that the chordates arose from relatively unspecialized worm-like forms. Indeed, forms like the nemertines are now seriously under consideration as the progenitors of the chordates. We have already examined this second possibility in our discussions of annelid, molluscan, onychophoran, and arthropod affinities. Further investigation of this thesis would take us into details of anatomy that we are unprepared to discuss at this time, and so we must leave the problem at this unresolved point.

Before turning to an examination of our prediction, let us attempt a two-step summarization of this survey of the major taxa. First, we shall try to organize the animal phyla into rather broad groupings based on their degree of anatomical complexity. Second, we shall investigate possible origins of these broad groups and of the phyla contained within them. We have, of course, already laid the groundwork of this topic by our comments on suspected affinities.

Grades of Animal Organization

The first and perhaps most obvious subdivision of the animal kingdom is the separation into acellular protozoa and cellular Metazoa. Among the Metazoa, we can immediately distinguish two further groups, the Parazoa, containing the single phylum Porifera (sponges), and the Eumetazoa, or true metazoans. The sponges present what has been called a cellular grade of organization; that is, although the sponge body is composed of many cells, they are never so highly integrated as to form tissues. Eumetazoa, on the other hand, characteristically are at the tissue level of organization.

Within the eumetazoans, further grades can be identified on the basis of body cavities. First, there are the acoelomate phyla, i.e., those phyla that possess no body cavity between the epidermis and gastrodermis. These phyla are the Platyhelminthes, Cnidaria, and Nemertina, of the ones we have examined. Second, there are the pseudocoelomate forms, of which we have discussed only the one phylum, Aschelminthes. Certain others, omitted here, are also pseudocoelomates. Third, there are the coelomate phyla, which are separable into schizocoelous and

enterocoelous phyla. The former group contains certain of the lophophorate phyla, the Annelida, Mollusca, Onychophora, and Arthropoda.
The latter contains the Brachiopoda of the lophophorate group, and the
Echinodermata, and Chordata. We should also point out that the acoelomate, pseudocoelomate, and schizocoelous coelomate groups are sometimes referred to as the Spiralia, because of the presence of spiral cleavage
in their embryogenesis.

It must be emphasized that these groupings are *not* taxa. They are
based on complexity of organization and disregard the question of
whether or not the various grades are monophyletic. Only in the Porifera
does the grade coincide with a taxon. In the case of the acoelomates, if
all the phyla of this level of organization have arisen from an ancient
acoeloid flatworm, and hence are monophyletic, then this grade could
have the same dimensions as a single large taxon (superphylum Acoelo-
mata?). These grades are presented as a useful way of grasping the apparent increase in complexity of animal form as one moves from protozoans to arthropods and chordates.

Phyletic Origins

Now there remains the ticklish problem of origins. Let us start
with the origin of the acellular animals. As we have said, the protozoa are
polyphyletic, and to reorganize their taxonomy, biologists will need the
help of botanists who understand the taxonomy of the plants—especially
the algal groups—from which the protozoa most probably arose. It may
well be that animal-like and plant-like acellular organisms will eventually
be included in the same taxon. Already we recognize that most algal
groups contain certain motile nonphotosynthetic forms that are only with
difficulty distinguished as algal rather than protozoan.

This raises a question we have completely ignored thus far, namely,
what is an animal? It is obviously easy to differentiate an elephant from
a tree, a snail from a fern, a jellyfish from moss, or even a ciliate from
colonial algae. We might say, then, that an animal is a nonphotosynthetic
organism capable of locomotion. But since all the sessile animals, such
as corals, various parasites, tube-dwelling worms, etc., do not move, we
have to eliminate the phrase "capable of locomotion." This leaves us
with "nonphotosynthetic organism," which, however, would mean that
nonphotosynthetic bacteria and fungi would be classified as animals, and
that colorless (nonphotosynthetic) flagellated algae would be in the
same category as colorless flagellated protozoa.

We think the dilemma is best solved in this way. First, we should
accept the fact that lower plants and animals are very closely related
forms. Second, we should admit that in simpler organisms the terms
"plant" and "animal" do not designate sharply definable taxonomic entities. Third, we should not use the terms Plantae (plants) and Animalia

(animals) or their equivalent to designate kingdoms, because these so-called taxa do not enable us to separate clearly the simpler plants from the simpler animals. Fourth, we should apply the term animal in a common-sense way to those organisms that are not photosynthetic and that are neither bacteria, fungi, nor colorless algae. We realize that it will be difficult to distinguish these latter forms from protozoa, and new criteria besides the presence or absence of photosynthetic pigments will have to be employed.

Fifth, the kingdoms might be reorganized along the following lines (a similar system, incidentally, was proposed in the nineteenth century by the biologist, Haeckel, a great student of phylogenetic problems): include the bacteria and blue-green algae, largely because of their unique nuclear apparatus, in the kingdom Monera; include the fungi, non-colonial algae, and protozoa in the kingdom Protista; include the colonial algae and all the higher plants in the kingdom Metaphyta; and include all the cellular animals, with the possible exception of the sponges (see below), in the kingdom Metazoa. Animals, then, would be members of two different kingdoms: the Protista (including the protozoans) and the Metazoa (including the cellular animals).

Theoretically, there are two ways in which the cellular or multicellular state could evolve from the acellular or unicellular condition. A colony of acellular forms could become so highly integrated that the colony as a whole functions as an individual organism, and thus becomes a cellularized individual. Or an acellular organism could become multinucleate, so that when cell membranes appear in the cytoplasm between the nuclei, a cellularized organism would result. Both of these modes have been suggested for the origin of the Metazoa from the acellular Protista. The sponges clearly seem to have arisen through colonial integration, either of zooflagellates or of a colonial green alga that lost its photosynthetic pigments.

In the Eumetazoa, both the Turbellarian flatworms and the Cnidarian planula theoretically have been derived from protistans. The planula is thought to have originated from a colonial green alga much like one of the possible sponge progenitors. Thus it, too, could be the result of colonial integration. The Turbellaria, on the other hand, probably have evolved from multinucleate ciliates that became cellularized. These last speculations are based on the assumption that cellularization took place within a single organism, but at this time we cannot definitely confirm these speculations.

We might summarize the situation in this way: (1) The sponges probably arose by colonial integration independently of cellular animals. Thus if the kingdom Metazoa contains the sponges and other cellular forms, it is at least diphyletic. Perhaps we should consider the sponge to be highly integrated, animal-like, protistan colonies, comparable to the highly integrated algal colonies, and thus remove the sponges from the

Metazoa, which would be left as a possibly monophyletic group. (2) The most primitive metazoan is probably either the cnidarian planula or the acoel turbellarian. (3) The attempts to derive the marine-dwelling, diploid, cellularized planula from fresh-water haploid, colonial green algae are not very fruitful. (4) The attempt to derive the marine, diploid, syncytial acoel from marine multimicronucleate (or diploid-nuclei) ciliates seems in many ways to be more valid than the alga-to-cnidarian scheme. It is difficult, although not unreasonable, to derive the cnidarian planula from the lower flatworms. In this volume, we shall take the position that the Metazoa (excluding the sponges) arose by the cellularization of a ciliate-like form to achieve a primitive turbellarian.

In our discussions of the origins of the phyla within the Metazoa, two important points stand out. The first is the key position of the acoelomate worms, and the second is the significance of developmental characters or larval morphology. Let us briefly comment on each of these in turn. Of the non-flatworm metazoan phyla that we have examined, there is not one phylum, with the possible exception of the Cnidaria, whose suspected affinities do not eventually lead us back to the Turbellaria. The pseudocoelomate groups are most likely derived from turbellarians. The same is true for schizocoelous coelomates, although for a group like the insects, onychophoran and annelid forms intervene, in that order, before the flatworms are reached.

The enterocoelous coelomates are a tougher problem, but here, too, our best guess might be that they originated from the nemertines and that these latter arose from the flatworms. But we must not rely too heavily on these speculations, for they are still just conjectures. Some of these affinities are excessively tenuous, such as those concerning the enterocoelous phyla. The seeming importance of the flatworms may simply arise by default—that is, because there are no other more likely ancestral forms—so we take the flatworms as the *most* likely candidates. This does not say how likely "most likely" is. In some cases, we know it is not very probable at all, but it is simply the best notion we have.

The significance of larval forms for phylogeny rests on two points. First, organisms develop by first laying down major body features that are then further and further elaborated during growth. For example, in a mammalian embryo, limbs begin to sprout just after the right and left sides are determined. After the limbs come paws or hands, and after these come digits, and then finally claws or fingernails. Second, viable changes only rarely occur in the early stages of development because such changes could affect the whole course of subsequent development and produce massive effects. Massive changes in delicately organized systems are not usually helpful; such systems are better modified by many successive small changes. And such small changes come about most often by mutations that affect only the later stages in development.

Thus the major features of an organism, which are laid down early, are evolutionarily quite conservative; they show little evolutionary change. This probably explains the presence of dorsal nerve cord, notochord, and gill clefts in all chordate embryos, although they are all highly modified or absent in adults. It explains why the bilateral larva, rather than the radially symmetrical adults, is used to suggest the affinities of the echinoderms and why the occurrence of spiral cleavage in platyhelminths, nemertines, aschelminths, annelids, molluscs, onychophorans, and perhaps in arthropods, is taken as a sign of evolutionary affinities in these forms.

To summarize these last two sections, we can say: The animal phyla can be organized into grades of organization that reflect different degrees of anatomical complexity. The least complex grade contains the protozoa or acellular, animal-like Protista. The Metazoa contains the remaining cellular animals, which can be placed in the broad categories of acoelomate, pseudocoelomate, and coelomate animals. This last grade also has two subdivisions that are based on the mode of coelom formation, schizocoelous and enterocoelous.

A discussion of the origins of the major animal groups reveals many taxonomic problems and many ideas of general biological interest. To name some of the more important ones: (1) The taxon kingdom Animalia should be eliminated and animals separated into the two kingdoms of Protista and Metazoa. (2) The origin of the Metazoa is obscure; this writer thinks the primitive metazoan was an acoeloid flatworm, but other views are more commonly held. (3) The flatworms are a plausible but not altogether convincing springboard for metazoan evolutionary radiation. (4) Developmental characters are of great help in unraveling phylogenetic problems.

The Prediction and Conclusions

In our last prediction, we stated that if evolution is an explanation for animal diversity, then we should be able to arange this diversity so it reflects the course of evolution. Such an arrangement is a phylogeny. The question now is: Can we construct a phylogeny and if so how plausible is it? The answer to the first part of the question is clearly, yes. The answer to the second part cannot be so definite. The phylogenies we put together today that deal with relations at the level of phyla and kingdoms are at best only careful speculations.

One way to illustrate the speculative nature of phylogenetic schemes is to compare several of them. The one favored by the author and which summarizes the important points of this chapter is given in Fig. 55. In another phylogeny that appears in Fig. 56, note the treatment of the protozoa, of the metazoans, and of the placement of the sponges and cnidarians. The authority who proposed this phylogeny, Professor Marcus of São Paulo University, Brazil, considers that all bilateral metazoans are

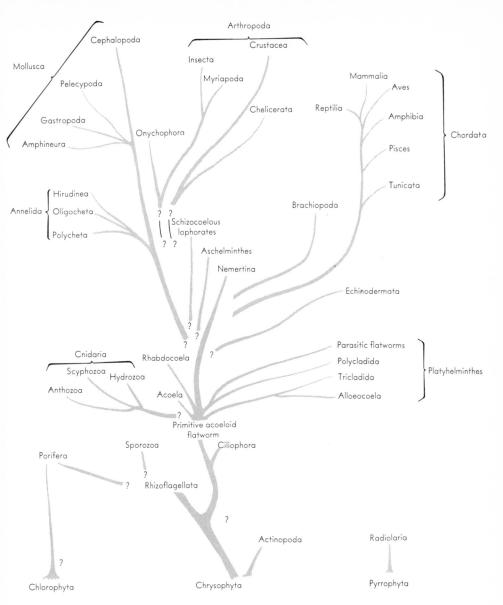

Fig. 55. A possible phylogeny of animals, summarizing the views emphasized in this volume.

coelomate and therefore that those forms which in our treatment are acoelomate really represent regressive or degenerative evolution of formerly coelomate organisms. The flatworms thus occupy a position very close to the annelids, molluscs, and arthropods.

A third phylogeny (Fig. 57), constructed by Professor Hadzi of Ljubljana University, Yugoslavia, can be called a straight-line phylogeny rather than the dichotomous or two-branched scheme of the first two figures. The "straight" line is achieved by deriving the enterocoelous forms from the schizocoelous ones. This means that mesoderm formation by outpocketing of the embryonic gastrodermis has evolved from mesoderm formation by separation of mesodermal masses into layers along the epi- and gastrodermis, respectively. Note the grades of organization: Ameria —without segments; Polymeria—many segments; Oligomeria—few seg-

Fig. 56. A second possible phylogeny of animals, which emphasizes the possibility that all bilateral metazoans are primitively coelomate forms (adapted from Marcus, 1958).

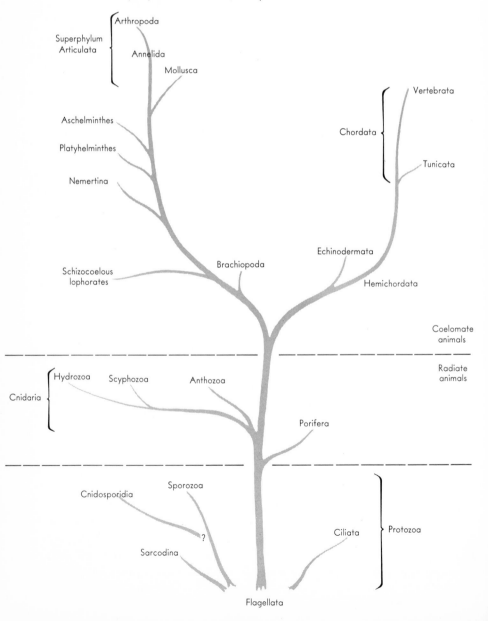

Fig. 57. A third phylogeny of animals, which emphasizes the so-called straight-line evolution (adapted from Hadzi, 1953).

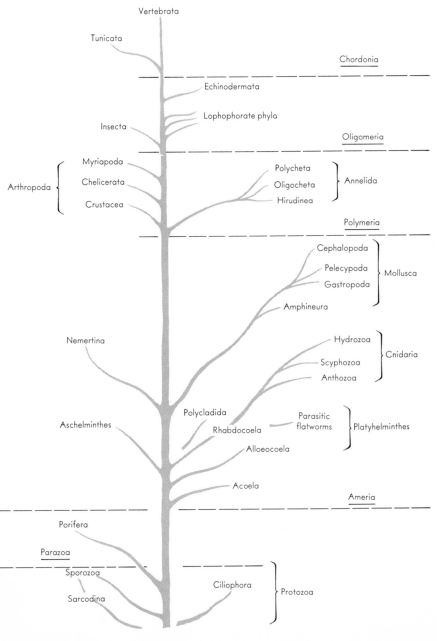

ments; and Chordonia—having a (noto-) chord. The variety of opinion shown in these three phylogenies indicates that mankind is still a long way from establishing an unquestionably valid phylogeny at the level of the higher taxa. There is presently only one area of agreement: that protozoa are close to the bottom of animal phylogeny, that cnidarians are among the primitive metazoans, and that arthropods and chordates are among the higher metazoans.

Does this mean our prediction is refuted? In one sense, yes; in another sense, no. It is refuted in that it is not possible as yet to present a widely acceptable evolutionary sequence. The reason for this failure is largely the incomplete nature of our data. In constructing a phylogenetic scheme, we are somewhat in the position of a person who is trying to reconstruct a tree when all there is to go on is a big pile of leaves. Our leaves can be compared to living species, the twigs represent genera, the thicker twigs, families, and so on till we come to the main trunk, or kingdom, which bears the whole variety of branches, twigs, and leaves.

In two ways the biologist's job is easier than that of the unhappy person reconstructing the tree from separate leaves. First, animal species show more variety of form than do the leaves from a single tree, and from this variety we can determine homologies. Second, animal fossils are very helpful guides in aiding us to trace out certain phylogenetic branches. But fossils tell us nothing about the evolution of such phylogenetically important groups of soft-bodied animals as the acoelomate worms. The heart of our phylogenetic problem is thus probably forever beyond the reach of any direct examination; inferences based on homologies of living forms are our *only* tool in this area. Therefore, we should expect difficulties in constructing a definitive and widely acceptable phylogenetic tree, for it must be based on homologies in organisms that initially diverged from each other well over half a billion years ago.

How, then, can we claim that in one sense our prediction is not refuted? We can because the data we *do* have are consistent with the idea of evolution. Since under the best of circumstances it would not be easy to trace affinities of evolving animals that originated in Pre-Cambrian times, it is not the weakness of our phylogenetic speculations in the higher taxa that is noteworthy, but the fact that we can make any suggestive speculations at all from the kind of data we have to work with.

Finally, let us recall that animal diversity can be arranged in grades. We have emphasized a scheme based on two criteria: (1) acellularity or cellularity and (2) absence or presence of body cavities. These grades, though they are not a phylogeny, do conform with a general principle of evolution we have mentioned several times, namely, that complex forms originated from relatively simpler forms. All the phylogenetic schemes discussed above are consistent with this general idea, although they may use somewhat different criteria to determine the degree of complexity— e.g., segmentation (Fig. 57) instead of body cavities.

Summary

This chapter has briefly described the higher taxa that are thought to be of major significance to phylogenetic problems. All phylogenies that have been proposed for the higher taxa are open to much criticism. Perhaps the most critical area of phylogeny is the evolutionary history of the soft-bodied worms. This group has no fossil history and so we must infer the events of more than 500,000,000 years ago by looking at modern forms, both adult and developmental. Because of the changes that are sure to have occurred in these half billion years, we must settle for imprecise conclusions.

The fact that a definitive phylogenetic scheme is not presently available does not mean that evolution is not responsible for animal diversity, but just the reverse. The continuing changes wrought by evolution are just what make the studies of phylogeny in the higher taxa so very complicated. Evolution, then, spurs us on to try to formulate phylogenetic trees and at the same time makes it very difficult to do so.

9

**Does
Evolution
Explain
Animal
Diversity?**

Only the last step now remains, to decide what we can conclude from the previous chapters in which we tested our predictions. First let us summarize the conclusions we arrived at in Chapters 6, 7, and 8, those chapters in which we examined, respectively, the predictions regarding temporal diversity, spatial diversity, and phylogeny.

Diversity in time: The fossil record clearly shows that large-scale change can occur as the result of many small, discrete changes; that animals become extinct; and that, in terms of their forms, animals diverge from one another and also converge. Whether or not they become more complex as time goes on is hard to say from fossil data.

Diversity in space: An ecological zoogeographic study shows that different types of animals adapt to specific ways of life; that ecological equivalents do occur; and that if we look at the generic or specific level, especially in mammals, we find that particular geographic areas contain distinct and characteristic fauna.

Phylogeny: No widely accepted evolutionary sequences can be established, as we can see from the many differences that exist in the proposals of different biologists. The disagreements arise largely from lack of data rather than from any doubt as to whether evolution did or did not occur; we concluded that evolution both spurred biologists to construct phylogenies and also made it
106

very difficult for biologists to create totally satisfactory phylogenies.

Since our predictions have not been completely fulfilled, we cannot conclude that Darwinian evolution is a wholly convincing explanation of animal diversity. On the other hand, we do not mean to reject evolution as an explanation. Just where, then, do we stand? To find out let us look again at the predictions we chose to examine.

At the outset, it should be realized that the predictions we selected were not the only ones possible. If we had so desired, we could have selected predictions that, at one extreme, would have been completely fulfilled, or, at the other extreme, would have been completely untestable and perhaps even unfulfilled. If we had taken the first alternative, we might now be concluding that evolution is indeed a satisfactory explanation of animal diversity. This would have followed, for example, if we had confined our attention *solely* to the first and third predictions of temporal and spatial diversity. But if we had made only the phylogenetic prediction, we would now be concluding that evolution is only a tenuously successful explanation of animal diversity. The degree of confidence we place in evolution as an explanation of animal diversity thus clearly depends on the predictions we select.

Furthermore, if our predictions have been aimed at a few minor problems and questions, then even if they are realized we would not be justified in accepting the hypothesis. If, however, the predictions are large in scope and touch on questions of broad, general significance and then are realized, we can be far more confident of our argument and can accept the explanatory hypothesis with minimal reservations. On this score, what about the predictions we are testing here? Are they trivial or broad in scope?

The answer is clear: our predictions are aimed at major problems. Indeed, it is difficult to conceive of any more comprehensive areas within the topic of animal diversity than those we have considered, namely, diversity in time and in space, and the whole evolutionary sequence from acellular to complex cellular animals. And within these broad areas, the predictions have raised basic questions, so basic that perhaps some of them may have seemed naive: Are some of the evolutionary changes produced by successive gene mutations? Is evolutionary development basically from simple to complex forms?

We might digress briefly at this point and ask why the author used the second prediction of spatial diversity (that different geographical areas, such as continents, have characteristic fauna), since it turned out to be imprecisely formulated and hence not testable. Surely, it might be said, the author of the book, finding the prediction to be badly worded, could go back and state the prediction properly. That, of course, could have been done, but the present form of the prediction was retained for two reasons. First, for the comprehension of the scientific method, it is more instructive to have some good and some bad predictions than to have all good ones. Second, what we learned about zoogeography and its bearing on evolution is still the same regardless of the formulation of the prediction.

Nevertheless, no matter how instructive or far-ranging our predictions are, many other predictions are still possible. For example, concerning the fossil record, we might have predicted, on the basis of known mutation rates and population sizes, possible rates of evolutionary change which we might encounter in a sequence of fossil forms. Or we could have predicted that the number of available niches limits animal diversity. The author did consider this as a possible point to be discussed, but omitted it because of the difficulty of defining precisely the nature of a niche. Or we could have made phylogenetic predictions within one of the larger taxa—for instance within the insects or crustaceans, or the birds or mammals—rather than between such taxa.

Since to test the predictions we had to draw upon many areas of animal biology—paleontology, ecology, morphology—these topics could only be treated very cursorily in this small book. We could not possibly present all the different interpretations of a given subject nor summarize all the data bearing on that subject. This brevity of treatment also warns us to be careful in drawing our conclusions.

Our final position might be stated in this way. The predictions we have examined are broad in scope, and they touch on problems of general importance. We are justified in having confidence in the conclusions we have drawn after testing these predictions, and we have found that most of the predictions have been fulfilled (i.e., the first and third predictions concerning temporal and spatial diversity). Those that were not fulfilled are of two types; either they were not completely testable because of lack of data (second prediction of temporal diversity and the problem of phylogeny), or they were imprecisely formulated (second prediction of spatial diversity). From the analysis in this short book, then, we find that we can accept evolution as an explanation of animal diversity, but that more information is needed and other predictions can and should be examined.

One additional point should be made. The fact that we established evolution as our explanatory hypothesis does not mean that other explanations are invalid. We have no space to explore this question further, but those interested should be encouraged to look for other explanations which are testable.

Postscript

We started this volume with the premise that humans need to understand. In our attempt to satisfy this urge concerning the external world of animals, we have investigated a wide array of animals, from the simplest to the most complex. We should realize that man himself is as much a part of that array as any other animal. He, too, has a fossil history and is continuously changing as he is acted on by the process of natural selection. He, too, is a leaf on a phylogenetic tree. But, in addition, man is the only thing on earth aware of this. He can ask himself questions that perhaps transcend all the others raised in this volume: What are the limits of the scientific method in achieving understanding? Can this method be used not only to understand man's position in the diversity of life but also to understand his need to understand?

Selected Readings

Part One: Introduction. The titles of the three books below indicate the nature of their contents. The third is more specialized than the others and is written from a scientist's rather than from a philosopher's viewpoint.

Campbell, N., *What is Science?* New York: Dover, 1952.
Butterfield, H., *The Origins of Modern Science, 1300–1800.* New York: Macmillan, 1957 (paperback edition).
Frank, P., *Philosophy of Science: The Link between Philosophy and Science.* Englewood Cliffs, N. J.: Prentice-Hall, 1957.

Part Two: Systematics. Both books are addressed to specialists but contain sections of general interest.

Mayr, E., E. G. Linsley, and R. L. Usinger, *Methods and Principles of Systematic Zoology.* New York: McGraw-Hill, 1953.
Mayr, E., ed., *The Species Problem.* Washington, D. C.: American Association for the Advancement of Science, 1957.

Survey of Animal Forms. These systematic introductions to invertebrates and vertebrates, respectively, are authoritatively written and beautifully illustrated.

Buchsbaum, R., *Animals without Backbones,* 2nd ed. Chicago: University of Chicago Press, 1948.
Romer, A. E., *Man and the Vertebrates.* Chicago: University of Chicago Press, 1941.

Part Three: Darwin and Evolution. The first volume is a selection of Darwin's works and includes fascinating excerpts from his *Autobiography.* The last volume is a modern statement of evolutionary theory.

Bates, M., and P. S. Humphrey, eds., *The Darwin Reader*. New York: Scribner, 1956.
Smith, J. M., *The Theory of Evolution*. Baltimore: Penguin, 1959.

Part Four: Paleontology. A leading authority presents his subject lucidly and enthusiastically in these two volumes.

Simpson, G. G., *Life of the Past*. New Haven: Yale University Press, 1953.
Simpson, G. G., *Evolution and Geography: An Essay on Historical Biogeography, with Special Reference to Mammals*. Eugene, Oregon: State System of Higher Education, 1953.

Ecology and Zoogeography. These two books, written for undergraduates and specialists, respectively, contain the basic information on these topics.

Odum, E. P., *Fundamentals of Ecology*, 2nd ed. Philadelphia: Saunders, 1959.
Darlington, P. J., Jr., *Zoogeography: The Geographical Distribution of Animals*. New York: Wiley, 1957.

Phylogeny. These three selections, and especially the first two, are written for experts. Both the first and second chapter of the third reference are recommended for their discussion of broad biological problems.

Hadzi, J., "An Attempt to Reconstruct the System of Animal Classification," *Systematic Zoology*, 2 (1953), 145–154.
Marcus, E., "On the Evolution of Animal Phyla," *Quarterly Review of Biology*, 33 (1958), 24–58.
Hyman, L., *The Invertebrates. Vol. I: The Protozoa through Ctenophora*. New York: McGraw-Hill, 1940.

Part Five: Conclusions. The first volume below includes a discussion of the ethical consequences of evolution. The second is a scientist's attempt to understand the significance of her own scholarly activity. The third is an imaginative and stimulating exploration of man's study of nature.

Simpson, G. G., *The Meaning of Evolution*. New Haven: Yale University Press, 1949. (Also available, somewhat abridged, as a paperback, Mentor Books, MD 66, and unabridged, Yale Paperbacks, Y23.)
Arber, A., *The Mind and the Eye: A Study of the Biologist's Standpoint*. New York: Cambridge University Press, 1954.
Weizsäcker, C. F., *The History of Nature*. Chicago: University of Chicago Press, 1949.

Index